Whatever It Takes

Le Bonheur Children's Medical Center:
The First Fifty Years

by Dale A. Berryhill

Published in 2006 by

The Urban Child Institute®
600 Jefferson Avenue Suite 200
Memphis, Tennessee 38105

Published in 2006 by

The Urban Child Institute®
600 Jefferson Avenue Suite 200
Memphis, Tennessee 38105

Manufactured in Korea

10 9 8 7 6 5 4 3 2 1   HC

LIBRARY OF CONGRESS CONTROL NUMBER 2005937850

The paper used in this publication meets the minimum
requirements of the American National Standards for Information
Sciences—Permanence of Paper for Printed Library Materials,
ANSI.48–1984.

Book design by Kathy Kelley, K Design / Oates Design

Dedication

This book is dedicated to all those who
have participated in the vision, creation,
growth, preservation, and use of
Le Bonheur Children's Medical Center.

The Le Bonheur Club Prayer

*ALMIGHTY GOD, who has called the
Le Bonheur Club to serve Thy little ones through
the ministry of healing, we ask Thy guidance
and direction in all of our endeavors. Bless the
Le Bonheur Children's Medical Center, its
patients, its staff and all who give of their time,
talent and treasure administering to the sick.
Deepen, we pray Thee, our commitment and use
us in Thy service, we ask in Thy name. Amen.*

Many of the things we need can wait.

The child cannot.

Right now is the time his bones are being formed,
his blood is being made, and his senses are being developed.

To him we cannot answer "Tomorrow."

His name is "Today."

Chilean poet Gabriela Mistral, 1945

Table of Contents

Appendices

CHAPTER ONE

A Unique Beginning

Memphis was a different place back in 1923. While the city limits extended to Graham and Goodlett, the majority of the city's 160,000 citizens lived within the boundaries of North, South, and East Parkway. Downtown was still the city's commercial and social center, and river commerce — especially the transportation of cotton to the world's markets — still formed the core of its economy.

Christian Brothers College was located at 612 Adams, Memphis University School was located at 23 S. Manassas, and St. Agnes Academy was located at the corner of Vance and Orleans. What later became the Mid-South Fairgrounds was then simply an open park called Montgomery Park. E. H. "Boss" Crump had already completed his six-year stint as the mayor of Memphis, but he was still solidifying his control over local and state politics.

The town of Raleigh had recently relinquished its charter and returned to unincorporated status, but a tram line still took excursionists out into the county to bathe in the Raleigh Springs. Raleigh's major thoroughfare would later be named for the governor of Tennessee at that time, Austin Peay.

Only recently had there been enough automobiles in the city for a restaurant called Fortune's to offer curbside service, thereby becoming one the world's first drive-in restaurants. The serialized letters of adventurer Richard Halliburton thrilled readers of *The Commercial Appeal.* Southwestern Presbyterian College — which would eventually change its name to Rhodes College — had not yet relocated to Memphis from Clarksville, Tennessee.

The city was poised to take part in the prosperity of The Jazz Age. Buildings under construction or just completed in 1923 included the Peabody Hotel, Lowenstein's Department Store, Ellis Auditorium, Methodist Hospital, and the Sears Building on Watkins. Piggly Wiggly founder Clarence Saunders had just completed his mansion on Central Avenue, although his bankruptcy the next year would lead to the mansion becoming the Pink Palace Museum. Also in 1923, the Junior League of Memphis was formed.

Four years earlier, in 1919, the city's centennial celebration had been especially joyful because World War I had just ended. But the celebration was short-lived, because returning veterans brought with them a Spanish influenza epidemic that killed more than 540,000 Americans and closed schools in Memphis for more than a year. The epidemic and the war left Memphis, like many other cities, with a high number of orphans. It is here that our story begins.

Facing page and above: The Memphis riverfront in the early 1920s.

Early photos of Leath Orphanage

"The Good Hour"

By January 1923, Leath Orphanage was filled to overflowing. Mrs. Allen Lacey and Mrs. Leslie Stratton were among the women who volunteered at Leath, and they were disturbed by the economic conditions of some of the children they saw there. They encouraged their daughters — Anna Lacey and Frances Stratton — to form a club to sew clothes for the children. The girls invited six of their friends to join, and other friends were soon added. The earliest official roster of the club (see next page) includes many prominent names in Memphis society both then and now.

One of the six friends in the original group, Elizabeth Jordan Gilliland, made two major contributions to the new club. First, she gave it its name. Having studied French in college and then having visited France, Elizabeth suggested that the group call itself "Le Bonheur." French for "happiness," the word is often translated literally as "the good hour." As son Bob Gilliland explains, "The idea developed that each hour spent with the children would be a 'good hour'." (French experts like Mrs. Gilliland pointed out that "the good hour" would actually be the feminine *la bonne heure*, but the idea was such a nice one that it stuck.)

Mrs. Gilliland's second contribution had an even more profound effect on the Le Bonheur Club's future. "Her brother was a polio victim at about age five," explains Bob, "and her father was a prominent Memphis businessman. I think it was Dr. Willis Campbell [founder of Campbell's Clinic] who came to him thinking he'd be a likely candidate to make a donation — and I believe the number I heard was $50,000 — to create the Crippled Children's Hospital." This family connection naturally led Elizabeth to suggest that the Club visit children in the Crippled Children's Hospital as well as in the orphanage. As a result, the Club began working with sick children from its earliest days.

In addition to sewing clothes for the children, the ladies of Le Bonheur began to mend dolls, then to make clothes for the dolls, as well. At the end of 1924, they held their first Christmas party for the children. The next year, they started the tradition of adopting specific children with extraordinary needs as special projects. In 1925, it was a little girl named Jewel. In 1927, it was a three-year-old girl with a club foot (whose name is now lost to us) for whom the ladies provided a home, clothes, a wheelchair, and other supplies during what turned out to be the last days of her life. In 1929, it was an amputee named Mollie Milligan for whom they provided a home, clothes, Christmas presents, and an artificial leg that they had to replace several times as she grew. Years later, the group had the privilege of sending Mollie to State Teacher's College, followed by the pleasure of attending her wedding.

By 1925, just two years after its beginning, the organization had grown to include 50 members, all of them young ladies prominent in Memphis society. Regular meetings were held at the University Club and monthly dues of twenty-five cents were levied. The next year, Le Bonheur was asked to serve as the main sponsor for the Children's Bureau, the government agency responsible for the coordination of care of all underprivileged children in the county. Representatives of Le Bonheur were placed on the Bureau's board of directors, and members regularly supplemented the Bureau staff in their daily duties. Le Bonheur members drove children to the dentist and doctor, held parties at holidays, and sponsored children for summer camp in Hardy, Arkansas. Before long they were serving as big sisters to every teenage girl at the Bureau. To fund these efforts, membership dues were raised in 1927 to one dollar a month.

In 1926, the group took on the task of running the Children's Bureau's fund-raising campaign, and they succeeded so well that they were awarded the Community Fund Silver Cup. Their success led to requests the next year to assist the Salvation Army and the Red Cross in their drives. In 1928 they won the Community Fund Silver Cup a second time, an exciting achievement for a group that had started so informally just five years before.

Le Bonheur Club Founding Members

Margaret Wherry Archer

Billie Anthony Carrington

Frances Stratton Cathey

Corneil Knight Chandler

Louise Fly Crump

Anna Lacy Davant

Mildred Donelson

Mildred May Elliotte

Madeline Fulton

Elizabeth Jordan Gilliland

Frances Bryan Gilliland

Carolyn Halliday

Evelyn Salmon Hopkins

Louise Ann Long

Annie Ruth Thompson
    McCaughan

Lucille Berwick Snowden

Marguerite Randolph Turner

Sara Maddux Van Fossan

Fay Ogilvie Wade

LE BONHEUR SEWING TO HELP NEEDY CHILDREN

Ply Their Needles on Garments That Are Give
To Wards of the Children's Bureau

Several times each month groups of Le Bonheur members meet to sew—mending and darning the used garments to be given needy children, wards of the Children's Bureau.

Co-chairmen of this committee are Mrs. W. W. Simmons Jr. and Mrs. Charles Clayton. So successful have been their efforts in collecting this clothing and having them made "almost like new" that a considerable sum of money has been saved by the Bureau. This money will be used in other ways to contribute to the happiness and health of these children. Clothes for children, from tiny babies to 'teen-aged boys and girls, are contributed to the bureau. There are the daintiest of baby dresses; snow suits and warm sweaters and many bright woolen skirts and frocks for girls of high school ages.

Mrs. Leslie Stratton (above) and her friend, Mrs. Allen Lacy, encouraged their daughters to start a sewing circle for orphans. The girls called their club "Le Bonheur," meaning "happiness" or "the good hour."

The ladies of Le Bonheur began to realize that they could reach far more children if they supplemented their own volunteer work with fundraising for a variety of organizations. They were, after all, well positioned for fundraising among the affluent citizens of Memphis. In 1929, the group added to its mission the raising of funds to provide services for needy children through their own or other organizations. Notably, the new policy specifically included provisions for children who could not afford healthcare. To facilitate this new role, in 1930 the Club became incorporated as a not-for-profit organization under the laws of the state of Tennessee.

Throughout the 1930s, the Club aggressively pursued its new policy, trying a variety of activities as it found its feet as a fundraising organization. A toy shop on Union Avenue called The Doll House was operated from 1930 to 1937. An annual Silver Tea event ran from 1931 to 1933. Sales of Little Theatre programs ran from 1930 to 1938. A Country Fair was held in 1938 and 1939. Members sold magazines, modeled in fashion shows, held rummage sales, entered floats in the Christmas and Floral Parades, and helped the Red Cross distribute clothing to victims of the flood of 1936.

Above: Every holiday season from 1930 to 1937, the Club ran a toy store as a fund raising activity. The small building that housed the store was designed and constructed by J. Frazer Smith, the architect who would later design the hospital.

Right: From its earliest days, the activities of the Le Bonheur Club received significant coverage in local newspapers, such as this 1946 full-page story from The Commercial Appeal.

4

The organization sponsored a Christmas House Lighting contest in 1931, a National Tennis Tournament in 1932, the Newspaper Guild program in 1934, and the opening of the Skyway on the roof of the Peabody Hotel in 1935.

The funds raised from these and many other activities went to a variety of charitable organizations and social services agencies. Some provided direct aid for individual children, such as a teenage girl whose nursing training was paid for in 1939. Other money went to specific programs, such as the "Baby Book" printed by the Club in 1934 and distributed free to new mothers. In 1940, a bed at the Crippled Children's Hospital was endowed in memory of two Le Bonheur members, Lucille Hurlburt and Irma Weathersby.

The organization's new emphasis on fundraising did not mean that it eliminated its work directly with children or its requirement that its members donate their fair share of "good hours." Members continued to work with the children of the Children's Bureau, and by 1933 the Club was providing a course in social service work to its members. By 1934 it was represented on the Council of Social Agencies. In 1937, it won the Della Robbia Plaque for having the most members on the Maternal Welfare Board. For four years beginning in 1938, the organization operated a boarding home for wards of the Children's Bureau. In 1942, the Club was providing direct aid to seventy children; by 1943 it was 118.

Le Bonheur members take wards of the Children's Bureau to the doctor's office for free examinations. Pictured in The Commercial Appeal *on January 2, 1944 are (left to right) Mrs. Mallory Morris, Mrs. J. Waldrup, Mrs. A. M. Crawford Jr., and Mrs. J. Nick Thomas Jr.*

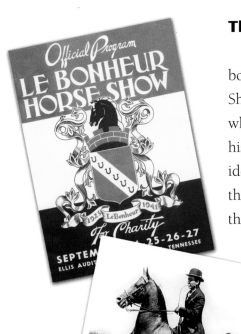

The Le Bonheur Horse Show

In 1939, Mrs. J. Everett Pidgeon, whose husband's family ran the Coca-Cola bottling plant in Memphis, had an idea for a new Le Bonheur fundraising event. She discussed her idea with fellow Club member Mrs. Raymond C. Firestone, whose husband had come to Memphis to run the Firestone plant in the interest of his family's firm. Both couples owned large stables of horses, and Mrs. Pidgeon's idea was for a first-class horse show in Memphis, with the proceeds going to fund the work of the Club. Their husbands enthusiastically offered their assistance, and the Club quickly adopted the idea.

The first Le Bonheur Charity Horse Show was held in 1940 under the auspices of the Memphis Horse Show Association, with Mrs. Pidgeon serving as general chairman. She achieved quite a coup when she secured top star Bob Hope to serve as master of ceremonies. In its very first year, the event raised $6,000 (enough money in those days to buy a home), and it was ranked fourth in the nation among equestrian events. In its second year, the show moved up to the number three spot. Actor/singer Dick Powell made an appearance along with his equally famous wife, Joan Blondell. More than 5,000 attended the opening night. An article from *The Commercial Appeal* demonstrates how quickly the show had established itself on the national circuit:

Bluebloods of Arena Parade As Socially Elite Line Boxes

Many Come for Le Bonheur's Showing of Nation's Finest Horses
The rhythmic prance of the thoroughbred feet around the ring yesterday afternoon and last night at Ellis Auditorium marked the opening of the second annual Le Bonheur Charity Horse Show with fine horses being shown from throughout the Nation. Officially opened last night by Mayor [Walter] Chandler and Mrs. Ira Allstadt, Jr., president of Le Bonheur, the show got off to an auspicious start

Right: The Le Bonheur Horse Show featured appearances by top stars of the day, including Dick Powell, Andy Devine, and Bob Hope.

Facing page: Miss Mary Jane Pidgeon, granddaughter of Mr. and Mrs. J. Everett Pidgeon (founders of the Le Bonheur Horse Show), with her horse Luise Rainer. Miss Pidgeon won more than 20 blue ribbons in the amateur three-gaited class on the national circuit. Here, she poses for a promotional photo for the Memphis Press-Scimitar *prior to the 1942 Le Bonheur show.*

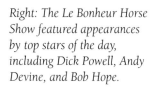

with hundreds of socially prominent guests attending. Boxes lining the ringside and decorated in the national motif of red, white, and blue bunting were filled with guests, many of whom had come thousands of miles to show or witness the performance of the high-stepping animals.

In 1942, with America newly engaged in World War II, the name of the event was temporarily changed to the Army and Navy Relief Horse Show, and $9,192 was donated to the Army and Navy Relief Fund. (In that year, the ladies of Le Bonheur also sold $200,000 in War Bonds.) Taking part were 264 entries from 26 states. The event was held outdoors at the Fairgrounds, and the championship stake was broadcast nationally over the NBC radio network. Gravel-voiced comedian Andy Devine served as master of ceremonies, as well as entering his horses in the competition. Amazingly, in just its third year, the event was ranked as the top horse show in the world.

The night before the show was scheduled to open in 1943, the Fairgrounds grandstand burned to the ground. It was rebuilt in a single day. "Ray Firestone sent every man from his factory," Club president Ada McDonnell Smith later recalled.

The idea for the Le Bonheur Charity Horse Show originated with Mrs. J. Everett Pidgeon.

THE COMMERCIAL APPEAL

MEMPHIS, TENN., FRIDAY MORNING, SEPTEMBER 7, 1945

Midnight Blaze Destroys Fairgrounds Grandstand, But Horse Show To Go O

The night before the 1943 show, the grandstand at the Fairgrounds burned down. With the help of lumber companies, plant workers, and local prisoners, it was rebuilt in a single day.

"The county sent convicts; lumber companies gave us lumber. The grandstand was built and decorated and the show was to go on, except that after all that, we were rained out the first night!" Even under such circumstances, the event was a success. By this time, it had grown into a gala affair that included fashion shows, cocktail parties, and a Junior Horse Show, activities that received pages of coverage in *The Commercial Appeal* and the *Memphis Press-Scimitar.* In 1944 it was rated "Most Beautiful Horse Show in America." In 1946, it raised the significant sum of $20,000. In 1948, it was featured in *American Horseman* magazine and was listed in the Encyclopedia Americana's annual supplement as one of the top ten equine exhibitions in the world. An article in *Independent Woman* magazine chronicled the role of the Club in establishing and running the event.

The Le Bonheur Charity Horse Show continued until 1948, then made a final appearance in conjunction with the Mid-South Fair in 1951. The reason for the event's demise was a simple one. The ladies of Le Bonheur had become involved in a much bigger project.

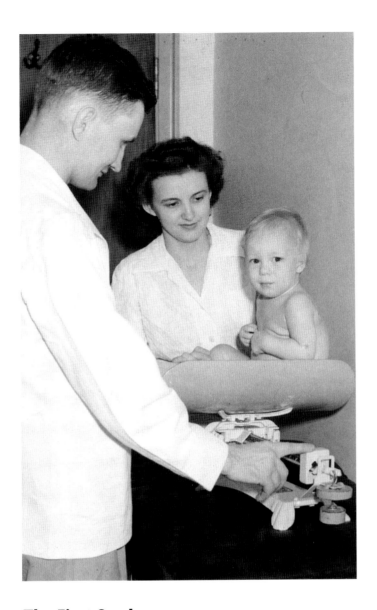

The First Seeds

In 1941, using the funds raised by the first Horse Show, the Le Bonheur Club established the city's first medical clinic for underprivileged children. Located in the Methodist Hospital Building, the clinic was open two mornings each week, and was staffed by private pediatricians who donated their time. A full-time nurse and a full-time social worker were soon added, their salaries paid from the proceeds of the Horse Show. These staff members went on house calls on days when the clinic wasn't open.

Due to the strict segregation demanded by society at that time, the original clinic served only white children. However, in January 1947, using funds raised by the Horse Show, the Club added extra days for Negro children. Characteristically, the Club's involvement with the children did not end with a physical examination. According to a 1945 article in *The Commercial Appeal*, "The club's follow-up service provides all necessary medicines, special diets and incidental expenses, and sees that codliver oil, tests and vaccinations, X-rays, blood counts, tonsillectomies, and other needed operations are provided. In addition to financing entirely this program, Le Bonheur members also give freely of their own time in transporting children and serving at the clinic." "We give them everything they need, from glasses to dental care," Mrs. J. D. Evans was quoted as saying in a 1947 article.

In November 1940, Le Bonheur announced the opening of the city's first medical clinic for underprivileged children, to be staffed by area pediatricians on a volunteer basis. The Club also operated foster homes (above) on behalf of the Children's Bureau.

Throughout the 1940s, the clinic occupied most of the time of the members. In its first four years of operation, there were 1,288 clinic visits. By 1948, the clinic was treating more than 1,000 children per year. In addition, the Club continued to work closely with the Children's Bureau, operating boarding homes and providing clothes and Christmas presents to children. By 1945, the Horse Show had paid the tab for 350 children in foster homes.

Working in the clinic, Memphis pediatricians discovered that the ladies of Le Bonheur were highly dedicated to the welfare of children and, just as important, that they had a seemingly unlimited ability to raise funds for worthy causes. In fact, by 1944, the Club had a reserve of $100,000 in its charity fund. It was in that year that Le Bonheur was approached by the Memphis Pediatric Society to discuss the need for a children's hospital. The ongoing war prevented any serious effort at that time, but the seed had been planted.

Le Bonheur's station wagon, which transported children to the Le Bonheur clinics, is pictured with a load of customers. At left are Mrs. J. D. Evans, Le Bonheur publicity chairman, Mrs. Allie Donovan, nurse in charge, and Mrs. James Hall, clinic chairman. Horse Show dollars paid for this and other welfare work of Le Bonheur.

A Unanimous Decision

The year after the war ended, the Le Bonheur Club decided to conduct a comprehensive analysis to determine its future. A Project Committee was formed to ascertain the way or ways in which the Club could best serve the area's children. Letters were sent to all area agencies that served children, asking for their input.

One of those letters went to the Memphis Pediatric Society, which in turn formed its own committee to identify the single most important project that the Society and the Club could undertake. The chairman of that committee was Dr. C. Barton Etter, whose wife was a Le Bonheur member (and later a founding partner of Coleman-Etter Real Estate). Dr. Etter summarized his committee's findings in an address to the Le Bonheur membership. Following are excerpts from that speech.

Madame President, Ladies of Le Bonheur:

The Project Committee of Le Bonheur, in making its survey of all possibilities that might aid Memphis children, contacted the president of the Memphis Pediatric Society, rightfully feeling that the pediatricians should best know what was most needed to better child care in this community. Our president in turn sent letters to each member asking that he state what, to the best of his knowledge, was the greatest single need which might be fulfilled. Subsequently, there was a called meeting of the Pediatric Society held specifically to select a project that would be acceptable to and worthy of an organization such as yours.

Believe me when I tell you that our meeting was not taken lightly. It lasted two hours, and I do not recall a single member leaving. A number of possibilities and certainly a number of definite needs were discussed: a rheumatic fever wing, homes for cerebral palsy, spastic victims, or epileptics were among worthwhile projects mentioned and freely discussed. Pro and cons, cans and cannots were heard from all sides. But when it came to making a decision, there was no dissension. The society voted unanimously — and wishes to go on record to that effect — that the greatest aid that could be given child welfare in this community would be to build, equip, and maintain a children's hospital here in Memphis. There are many reasons why we need a children's hospital in Memphis, but I would like to elaborate on three:

First, there are not nearly enough hospital beds in Memphis devoted to the care of children. Formerly, all three major hospitals in Memphis had floors or wings set aside for the care of children, so we never had trouble getting a sick child into the hospital. In the present crowded conditions, this is not true. There is currently not a hospital in Memphis that has a pediatric section devoted strictly to pediatric cases except for the ward rooms. When the hospitals are crowded, adult patients are put on pediatric floors. I have personally seen seven adults in a possible nine pediatric rooms. I cannot blame the hospitals for this; they are simply answering the greatest constant demand for beds. But it does not help your feelings as parents, or our feelings as pediatricians, when we cannot hospitalize your child for pneumonia because some adult [got] the last vacant pediatric room just before your child became ill.

Believe me, this happens. There are times when we cannot get a pediatric patient into any hospital, regardless of the seriousness of his illness or your willingness to pay. If we are having trouble accommodating our private patients, if you parents who are willing and able to pay any necessary amount to get proper attention for your children are unable to find adequate facilities, what chance do you think the indigent child has? If facilities are scarce for private patients in private hospitals, you must realize that they are even scarcer for the group for whom your

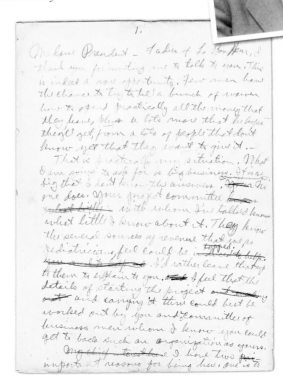

Dr. Barton Etter and the handwritten draft of his speech to Le Bonheur proposing the establishment of a children's hospital in Memphis

Mrs. Leslie M. Stratton, Jr. (third from right), daughter-in-law of one of the Club's founders, was president in 1947 when the Club voted to undertake the building of a children's hospital. Her successor, Mrs. Charles Gerber (third from left) presided over the hospital's pivotal capital campaign. Other officers in 1948 were (left to right) Mrs. Walker McLemore, Mrs. Cooper Turner, Jr., Mrs. Charles T. Clayton, and Mrs. Harold High. (Photo from The Commercial Appeal, *January 11, 1948)*

organization has always worked so hard. A children's hospital would furnish more private and charity beds for the children of our community while simultaneously freeing up hospital beds for adults in the existing hospitals.

The second reason we need a children's hospital in Memphis is that we are far behind most cities our size in equipment and facilities for doing research and diagnosis in pediatrics. There are 22 pediatricians in Memphis and there is not one of us who has not at sometime had to send a patient to Nashville, St. Louis, Chicago, Baltimore, or Boston for diagnosis or treatment. Frankly, we resent this, and we consider it a reflection of our city, our hospitals, and our University. We preach to the Tri-State physicians through their medical meetings and journals that we are a medical center, yet when it comes to a difficult problem in pediatrics, we let them down. With a children's hospital — one designed to qualify as a full-time teaching and research hospital — we would no longer have to send sick children on long trips to other cities.

Third, pediatric expertise is thinly spread throughout the community's hospitals. We have three private hospitals in Memphis and one city hospital. Each of these four hospitals must have a certified pediatrician in attendance at all times to maintain its rating by the American Hospital Board. Some hospitals require two at a time. We serve three or four month stints at four hospitals, and some pediatricians do not serve at all hospitals, so you can see how thinly our lines are drawn. A children's hospital would allow us to centralize pediatric teaching, research, diagnosis, and treatment efforts and to devote our attentions to building up a pediatric center worthy of our city.

I am authorized to offer you the whole-hearted cooperation of the Memphis Pediatric Society and to assure you that we will gladly staff the hospital and offer it the complete backing required to make it comparable to any children's hospital that now exists. We firmly believe that if you will undertake such a project and throw your weight or your unlimited energy and ability behind it, you cannot help but erect a hospital comparable in size and quality with those in other cities of this size. It will be a hospital where you can take care of those needy children that your society has always sought to help. It will be a hospital that you would be proud to have known as Le Bonheur Children's Hospital.

Thank you.

Immediately following this address, the membership of Le Bonheur voted unanimously to undertake the establishment of a children's hospital in Memphis. The Pediatric Society was soon to discover that it had gone to the right group of women to make its dream a reality.

Elizabeth Gilliland, The "Grande Dame" of Le Bonheur

She didn't initiate the founding of the Le Bonheur Club. She never served as its president. Yet Elizabeth Jordan Gilliland probably did more to shape the destiny of Le Bonheur than anyone else. Who was this distinguished lady, who came to be known as the "grande dame" of Le Bonheur?

Elizabeth Jordan was born on September 18, 1898 in Savannah, Georgia. Her family moved to Memphis when she was seven years old. Her father, Robert H. Jordan, was in the tobacco and automobile business. A successful business leader, he helped secure financing for the Harahan Bridge across the Mississippi River by personally pledging his assets to assure the bond sale. Because his son, Robert, Jr., had polio, he helped finance the new Crippled Children's Hospital.

Elizabeth attended the Hutchison School in Memphis. Upon graduation, says her son Jim, "She went to National Cathedral School in Washington and Finch College in New York. Then in 1920 she went to Europe." "She studied French in both schools," adds Bob Gilliland, Jim's brother. "That was the second language in those days. It was the language of worldwide diplomacy." This experience led her to name the club she helped form in 1923. Then, because of her family's connection to the Crippled Children's Hospital, she guided Le Bonheur into its first involvement with children's healthcare.

In 1924, Elizabeth married Frank M. Gilliland, a prominent Memphis attorney. The couple had three sons,

Frank, Jr., Jim, and Bob. Frank, Jr. and Jim became attorneys like their father, with Jim serving as general counsel for the U.S. Department of Agriculture. Bob was a military pilot and later a test pilot for Lockheed. (The senior Mr. Gilliland died in 1959, and Frank, Jr. died of a heart attack in 1984.)

Having given the Club its name, she was a stickler for its proper French pronunciation throughout her life. When the hospital was being built, she actually visited radio and television stations throughout the city to ensure that the on-air personalities knew the correct pronunciation of "Le Bonheur." "I don't think there was ever a single occasion in which the word was mentioned, either in conversation or listening to television, that she didn't shake her head about it and correct it," says her son Bob. "And," he adds with a chuckle, "our brother Frank used to imitate her behind her back doing the proper pronunciation." Although Elizabeth's tutoring failed to preserve the name's French heritage for the population at large, most members of the generation who helped found the hospital still use the proper pronunciation to this day.

At the dedication of the hospital's Tree of Life donor recognition wall sculpture in 1982, Mrs. Gilliland joked that the only time she had heard the hospital's name properly pronounced was when they were invited to Paris to represent Le Bonheur at a medical exposition in 1956. But then she added, "I want to say now that it

Elizabeth Gilliland in her teens.

doesn't matter how you pronounce it. It is always the same: The Good Hour. You may call it anything you want to. It may be the Hour of Happiness, the Sharing and Caring Hour, the Friendship Hours, the Sewing Hour — they are all Good Hours."

When Elizabeth passed away in 1996 at the age of 97, the Memphis *Commercial Appeal* honored her with a banner headline write-up. Through the years, the Gilliland family has continued to make generous contributions to the hospital, funding such projects as the Tree of Life sculpture and a 50th-anniversary history video, both of which are dedicated to the memory of Elizabeth Gilliland.

Elizabeth with her son, Jim, and founding Le Bonheur board member Palmer Brown.

Elizabeth Gilliland on one of her many trips abroad.

"The Easiest Campaign"

Building a world-class children's hospital from the ground up was going to be an expensive undertaking, but the ladies of Le Bonheur were undeterred. Within weeks after approving the project, the members of the Club's Hospital Committee met with officials of the University of Tennessee College of Medicine to discuss how building funds might best be raised.

With the total cost of the hospital estimated at $1,870,000, it was obvious that state and federal aid would be essential. Envoys sent to Nashville met with the appropriate agencies that handled both state funds and the federal Hill-Burton funds. In 1949, state and federal matching funds totaling $1,421,200 were pledged to the project. Federal Hill-Burton funds would account for 52% of the total, or $972,400, while state funds would provide 24%, or $448,800. These funds were contingent upon the raising of the remaining 24%, another $448,800. But with $200,000 pledged by the Crippled Children's Hospital and $42,000 raised by a huge land reclamation project out on New Brunswick Road, the Club only had to raise $206,800 in order to qualify.

In the meantime, the proper location of the hospital had become a matter of debate between the "town and gown" factions within the medical community. Some of the private pediatricians wanted the hospital adjacent to one of the large private hospitals, while those on staff at the University of Tennessee (UT) argued that the new hospital should be close enough to serve as a pediatric teaching and training center for students, interns, and residents. The Memphis Pediatric Society held a special meeting to consider the matter. After a heated debate, the Society voted to recommend a location close to the University of Tennessee.

As it turned out, a brief scare in the summer of 1949 led to a direct affiliation between Le Bonheur and UT before the hospital was even incorporated. In July, the Memphis city government announced that it would not fund the ongoing operation of the hospital, something the Club had apparently assumed. Club president Beatrice Gerber was quoted in *The Commercial Appeal* as saying that, unless a solution could be found, she would propose notifying the state Health Department to release the funds being held for the project. When UT announced that it would help handle the hospital's charity cases, and studies showed that the hospital could be self-sustaining otherwise, the project was back on.

In November of 1949, application was made to incorporate the hospital as a not-for-profit organization governed by a board of directors appointed by the Club. Incorporation was a necessary step to qualify for the government funds and to initiate a capital funds campaign. A charter was granted by the state, and on December 8, the board met with attorney Walter Chandler to finalize the incorporation.

With this step taken, the city of Memphis and the Shelby County government announced that they would make available through a long-term lease the land on the east side of Dunlap between Washington and Adams. The cost? One dollar per year.

The capital fund drive — which kicked off on December 29, 1949 — was headed by Allen Morgan, Sr., executive vice-president of First National Bank (now First Tennessee). Palmer Brown III, who would serve on the hospital's first board of directors, recalls his brief stint as chairman of the Major Contributions Committee: "I invited twenty of the least likely to accept men in Memphis, including the presidents of all three major banks," he says. "The promise I made to them was, 'There will be one luncheon. It will last no more than an hour and a half. There will be no follow-up, no additional meetings. That will be it.' Nineteen of the twenty showed up." Brown made his pitch, then closed by saying, "Let's get it over quickly. Let's report back in one week's time and get it done. The cards are on the table over there. And I'm giving you back five minutes because we have five minutes left from our hour and a half."

"Within a week," Brown says, "they had over-subscribed and the whole thing was over. It was the easiest campaign I ever conducted in my life."

When the capital fund campaign officially concluded on February 18, 1950 — less than two months after it began — it was over-subscribed by $50,000. Raymond C. Firestone — one of the initiators of the Le Bonheur Horse Show — pledged $10,000 even though he had been transferred back to his company's Akron, Ohio headquarters during the drive. Firestone also agreed to serve on the hospital's first board of directors, of which J. Everett Pidgeon was chairman. That board, one third of which were Le Bonheur Club members, was filled with the names of Memphis's oldest families and most prominent businessmen.

First Board of Directors of Le Bonheur Children's Hospital, Inc.
(1949-1950)

J. Everett Pidgeon, *Chairman*

Raymond C. Firestone

Allen Morgan, Sr.

Palmer Brown III

J. Thurston Roach

S. Toof Brown

J. T. Russell

Walter Chandler

R. B. Snowden

C. J. Wagner

Jack Goldsmith

Norman Isenberg

William Kent

Vance Norfleet

Clyde Patton

Robert H. Peoples

Mrs. Ceylon B. Frazer

Mrs. Price Curd

Mrs. Charles Gerber

Mrs. J. Everett Pidgeon

Mrs. Howard Pritchard

Mrs. Thomas Gaines

Mrs. David Saxon

Mrs. Frank Weathersby

Le Bonheur Hospital Assured--Fund Over Top by $50,000

100-Bed Institution for Children: One of City's Speediest Drives

The Le Bonheur Children's Hospital fund campaign went over the top today by $50,000, Allen Morgan, general chairman, said.

Mr. Morgan told several hundred

Building a Building

With the money raised and government funds assured, the hospital's new board of directors quickly established a building committee to oversee construction. Chaired by Jack Goldsmith, the committee included Vance Norfleet, Mrs. Price Curd, Mrs. Charles Gerber, and Mr. and Mrs. J. Everett Pidgeon.

For the hospital's design, the Club turned to prominent Memphis architect J. Frazer Smith, husband of Club member Ada McDonnell Smith, the lady who had been president the year the grandstand burned down. Mr. Smith had already involved himself in Club efforts, as when he had designed and built the Club's Doll House toy shop several years before. In designing the children's hospital, he was assisted by his daughter, Sue Cheek Hughes, also an architect and also a member of the Club. "I started working for my father as soon as I graduated from college, which was 1948," recalls Mrs. Hughes, "and one of his first commissions that I participated in was the Le Bonheur Children's Hospital. We interviewed pediatricians and cardiologists and anesthesiologists and every medical profession that would have anything to do with children."

To assist Smith and his associates, a medical advisory committee was appointed that included Dr. Tom Mitchell, Dr. Barton Etter, Dr. James Hughes, Dr. James Ettledorf, and Dr. Walter Ruch. "They went all over the United States looking at children's hospitals, what worked, what didn't work," says Mrs. Hughes. "What would you like to have if you were doing a children's hospital all over again? So with all this input from everybody, we started working the plans."

The first architectural sketch of the hospital was unveiled to the public on February 5, 1950, in the middle of the fundraising campaign. With the money raised and land secured, construction bids were let out immediately. Less than five months after the fundraising campaign topped its goal, construction began.

Architect J. Frazer Smith

Below: Le Bonheur's Architectural Team. J. Frazer Smith (seated, center) looks over the plans for the new Le Bonheur Children's Hospital along with his associates, which include his daughter, Sue Cheek Hughes, Zeno Yeates (left), and Dave Haaga.

The groundbreaking ceremony was held on July 2, 1950. Two small children from the Children's Bureau wielded a golden shovel, but the ground had been baked so hard by the blazing sun that they were unable to make a dent in it. As Dr. James Hughes later put it, "Elders came to the rescue, perhaps symbolic of the help the older generation gives to the younger in affording health facilities." Hughes says the ceremony was punctuated by low-flying propeller airplanes and bulldozers demolishing buildings along the street to make way for the new children's hospital.

Construction took two years. As so often happens with such projects, the initial cost estimate of $1,870,000 proved to be somewhat optimistic. The final price tag was around $2,220,000. Luckily, the original fundraising campaign had oversubscribed by $50,000, and the Club was able to donate $25,000 from the proceeds of the 1951 Le Bonheur Horse Show. The remainder was eventually made up through additional donations.

Top: The original architectural sketch of Le Bonheur Children's Hospital.

Center: Fittingly, two children who had been helped by the Club wielded the golden shovel at the hospital's groundbreaking.

Right: The hospital under construction.

The "Founding Fathers" of Le Bonheur

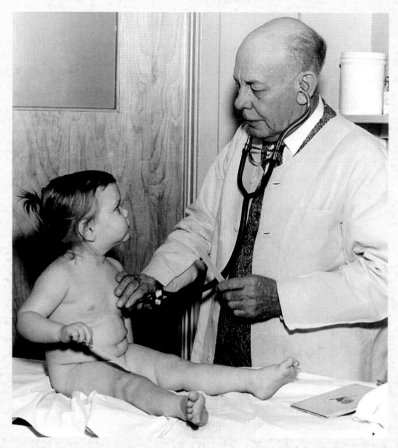

Dr. Tom Mitchell

DR. FRANK THOMAS MITCHELL was chief of the Division of Pediatrics at the University of Tennessee College of Medicine from 1940 to 1960. He pushed for the creation of Le Bonheur Children's Hospital, served on its design committee, and was elected its first chief of staff. Dr. Mitchell received his medical degree from UT in 1914 and joined the staff of the College of Medicine in 1917, serving first as outpatient director for the old Memphis General Hospital. He served as president of the Tennessee State Pediatric Society and was elected head of the American Medical Association's section on pediatrics in 1955. Two years earlier, his associates had already honored him by presenting his portrait to the University of Tennessee, where it still hangs today.

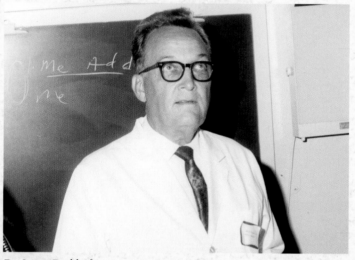

Dr. James Etteldorf

DR. JAMES HUGHES, internationally known for his medical textbooks on pediatrics, served as the hospital's third chief of staff. A graduate of the University of Tennessee College of Medicine, he was Chairman of the UT Department of Pediatrics from 1960 until 1975. He was appointed to serve as Le Bonheur's first Medical Director when that position was created in 1972. In 1976, he founded and was the first director of the Center for Children in Crisis. During his career, he was president of the American Academy of Pediatrics, received the Legion of Merit for his service as a brigadier general running military hospitals in Italy and Africa during World War II, and was appointed a consultant on children's health to the World Health Organization.

Dr. James Hughes

DR. JAMES ETTELDORF became the first full-time professor of pediatrics at the University of Tennessee in 1945. He was a strong advocate of the establishment of Le Bonheur Children's Hospital and served as its fourth chief of staff. In 1959, he secured a ten-year grant from the National Institute of Health that was instrumental in the development of pediatric subspecialty training at the University of Tennessee and Le Bonheur. He served as Secretary-Treasurer of the American Board of Pediatrics, but is best remembered for his legendary "Duck Dinners," an annual event much anticipated by the Le Bonheur medical staff and UT faculty.

DR. BARTON ETTER, a community-based pediatrician, chaired the Pediatric Society's committee that recommended to the Le Bonheur Club the establishment of a children's hospital in Memphis. He then served on the hospital's design committee. Elected secretary of the medical staff when the hospital opened, he served as the hospital's second chief of staff. He was also an officer in the Tennessee chapter of the American Academy of Pediatrics.

Dr. Barton Etter

"Absolute Joy"

On June 15, 1952, a dedication ceremony was held at the entrance of the hospital at 849 Adams Avenue. It was a windless, bright, blistering hot June day, so hot that the ladies' shoe heels sank into the new asphalt pavement. Gaily colored gas-filled balloons made a beautiful backdrop for the ceremony, but before things had progressed very far, the heat caused the balloons to begin bursting with a noise like firecrackers. They had to be taken into the air-conditioned interior of the building so the speakers could be heard.

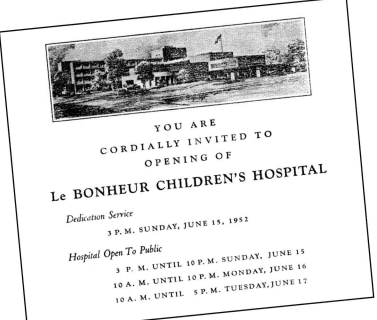

YOU ARE CORDIALLY INVITED TO OPENING OF

Le BONHEUR CHILDREN'S HOSPITAL

Dedication Service
3 P. M. SUNDAY, JUNE 15, 1952

Hospital Open To Public
3 P. M. UNTIL 10 P. M. SUNDAY, JUNE 15
10 A. M. UNTIL 10 P. M. MONDAY, JUNE 16
10 A. M. UNTIL 5 P. M. TUESDAY, JUNE 17

Nevertheless, not only were many of the Le Bonheur Club present, but also numerous friends of the Club, physicians, representatives of the University of Tennessee, members of the Hospital Board, and interested citizens. The principal speaker was Dr. Warren W. Quillion, the president of the American Academy of Pediatrics. J. Everett Pidgeon, chairman of the board, also spoke, as did Dr. O. W. Hyman, University of Tennessee Vice-President, who envisioned Le Bonheur as an important link in establishing in Memphis a group of hospitals and clinics which would "eventually become worthy of the designation, 'Medical Center.'"

Below: The hospital's dedication ceremony is opened by Allen Morgan, Sr., who had served as general chairman of the fundraising campaign.

"Mayor Watkins Overton officially opened the hospital that hot June day," says Elise Pritchard, Le Bonheur Club president at the time. "There were doctors from all over the United States who came to see the hospital. We had a nice group there that day. Just joy, just absolute joy to know that the hospital was really in existence."

The climactic moment came when Mrs. Pritchard gave a gracious speech, then made a symbolic gesture that has become forever associated with the spirit of Le Bonheur. "We had about 10 or 12 balloons and we tied the keys to the hospital to them," she recalls. "I made a little speech about the hospital never being closed to any child, and I let the balloons go and the keys with it. That was the opening of the hospital. The hospital would be open, never closed, to any sick child. And it never has."

The idea was for the balloons to rise majestically and carry the keys far away into the sky, but in the hot, windless day, the balloons rose only slightly and then went floating down Adams Avenue, almost descending into the street. Just as the crowd was beginning to think that a bad omen had occurred, the balloons miraculously began to rise and float upward and onward, and the doors of Le Bonheur Children's Hospital were opened forever to the children of Memphis and the Mid-South.

Below: Club president Elise Pritchard releases balloons with the keys to the hospital attached, symbolizing that the doors of Le Bonheur would never be closed to any sick child. Standing next to her is Mayor Watkins Overton, who officially opened the hospital.

Facing page: This aerial photo of the newly completed hospital shows its proximity to the rest of the Memphis Medical Center. Notice that the hospital was originally surrounded mainly by private homes.

UNION

Scottish Rite Building

Baptist Hospital

University of Tennessee

MADISON

Russwood Park

John Gaston Hospital

Tobey Hospital

Regional Medical Center (The Med)

DUNLAP

West Tennessee Tuberculosis Hospital

ADAMS

Le Bonheur Children's Hospital

CHAPTER TWO

1952-1969

The Early Years

I n the twenty-nine years between the founding of the Le Bonheur Club in 1923 and the opening of the hospital in 1952, the population of Memphis more than doubled to nearly 400,000, with new suburbs extending as far east as Mendenhall. In 1949, Poplar Plaza, the city's first major suburban commercial development, opened at the corner of Poplar and Highland. The following year, East High School opened its doors, and Second Presbyterian Church moved from its original location at Hernando and Pontotoc to the corner of Poplar and Goodlett. In 1951, St. Agnes Academy moved from Vance and Orleans to the corner of Walnut Grove and Mendenhall.

The year the hospital opened, a Memphis businessman named Kemmons Wilson opened the world's first Holiday Inn on Summer Avenue. Memphis won the award for the "Nation's Quietest City" for the second year in a row, and it was in the middle of a twenty-four-year run of being declared the "Nation's Cleanest City." As they had in 1923, Memphians were enjoying a post-war period of prosperity and low crime. The opening of Le Bonheur Children's Hospital was seen as a crowning touch in Memphis's effort to establish itself as a major city.

The hospital did not actually open for a week after the dedication ceremony, in order to give the public a chance to tour the 89-bed facility. Everyone agreed that J. Frazer Smith had designed a children's hospital that was second to none. In fact, later that year it was selected as one of thirty outstanding American architectural designs by the American Institute of Architects. In December 1954, it was featured by *Modern Hospital* magazine as the Hospital of the Month, based on its beautiful architecture and functional arrangement. In 1956, it was the only children's hospital in the United States chosen to have representation at the International Seminar on Children's Hospitals, held in Paris. In 1957, it was featured in *La Revue*, a French hospital magazine.

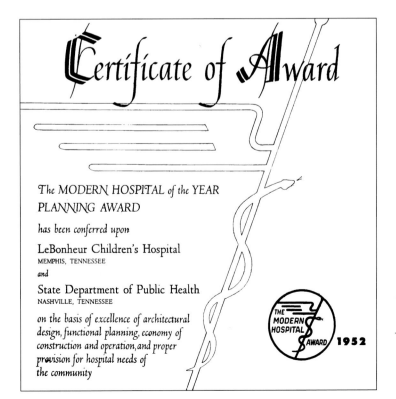

Certificate of Award

The MODERN HOSPITAL of the YEAR PLANNING AWARD

has been conferred upon

LeBonheur Children's Hospital
MEMPHIS, TENNESSEE

and

State Department of Public Health
NASHVILLE, TENNESSEE

on the basis of excellence of architectural design, functional planning, economy of construction and operation, and proper provision for hospital needs of the community

THE MODERN HOSPITAL AWARD 1952

The new Le Bonheur Children's Hospital was recognized by both Modern Hospital *magazine and the American Institute of Architects for its beautiful and functional design.*

"As Modern as it Could Be"

At the hospital's opening, *The Commercial Appeal* gave it several pages of coverage, including many large photographs featuring Le Bonheur Club ladies as models. The stories were glowing in their description of the facility. The building offered four floors of patient rooms with "solar control," which the newspaper described as concrete overhangs to keep the summer sun out of rooms, but "permit it to have full play" in winter. J. Frazer Smith was quoted as saying, "Each room in the four nursing units faces south so young patients will get a maximum of sun during the winter and none during the summer."

Four rooms had adjoining "apartments" for parents, one per floor, reported the paper. Patient rooms had wall microphones "which can pick up even the tiniest wail [and] convey it instantly to the nurses' station." Near the main lobby was the "Department of Recreational Therapy, where recuperating youngsters may play to their heart's content." In addition, "Children can step through a small door to a large play terrace…to their own large playground…with slides, swings and see-saws."

"It's not necessary to put in a hurried call for an oxygen tank when an emergency arises," said the newspaper, "for oxygen is piped to every room." The building's pneumatic tube system, "like that seen in some department stores, carries equipment, supplies and medical records and messages all over the big institution

Above: A pneumatic tube system allowed fast communication between floors.

Right: Le Bonheur Club member Gloria McPhillips Andereck (rear) gives a tour of the new hospital to interested Memphians.

Facing page, top: Former Le Bonheur Club president Beatrice Gerber models a patient room for The Commercial Appeal.

with split-second timing." The newspaper story concludes, "When a doctor needs something, he gets it in a hurry."

According to *The Commercial Appeal*, there were initially "three major and three minor" operating rooms. The hospital was equipped with the latest in medical technology, including EEGs, a broncoscopic room, a training clinic for post-polio and birth injury cases, and genito-urinary and orthopedic departments. As Le Bonheur Club president Elise Pritchard put it later, "The hospital was as modern as it could be at the time."

The Bunny Room

The most talked-about feature of the new hospital was The Bunny Room, a Le Bonheur Club innovation that had been incorporated into the hospital plans. Located adjacent to the operating rooms, The Bunny Room featured shelves lined with toys. Children going into surgery would be wheeled through The Bunny Room, where they were allowed to choose any toy. By the time the choice was made and the child was cuddling his or her new toy, the anesthesia had started its work, and all pre-surgery jitters would be left to the parents.

"The Bunny Room was a brilliant thought on the part of the Le Bonheur Ladies," says Dr. Ray N. Paul, Pediatric Cardiologist (retired). "It did a whole lot to ease children. They got to pick out a toy and carry it along with them. When they came to in the recovery room they had their toy there. It did a lot to help kids."

Far right: The caption for this photo from the June 16, 1952 Memphis Press-Scimitar read, "Before going to surgery, a young patient would first be taken to The Bunny Room where Miss Dorothy Akers, operating room superintendent, would give him a toy or a doll that he might keep. Another name for The Bunny Room was the anesthetic department."

Hospital of the Year

Memphis was justly proud of its new hospital, which the *Memphis Press-Scimitar* called "one of the most modern hospitals in the country." This claim was confirmed when the facility was declared "Hospital of the Year" by *Modern Hospital* magazine.

Above and above right: The original entranceway to Le Bonheur Children's Hospital, located at 848 Adams Avenue.

Right: The facility's clean lines and warm atmosphere kept it from seeming dated for many years.

When first entering the hospital, visitors were greeted by the sounds and smells of the Coffee Shop.

Above: Looking back toward the entrance, the hospital's coffee shop can be seen through the windows on the left.

Left: The receptionist doubled as the hospital's telephone operator, manning an old plug-style switchboard.

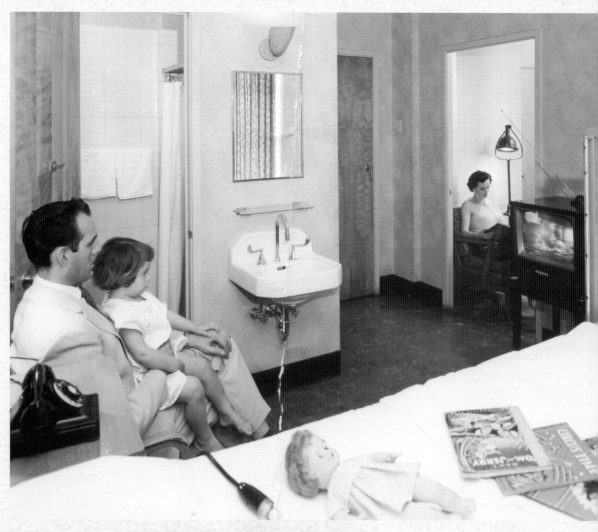

Some patient rooms had
adjoining apartments
for parents.

The hospital was designed so that
patient rooms would receive
maximum sunlight in winter and
maximum shade in summer.

*The hospital's
original medical
amphitheater,
patterned after
the old European
style, was
affectionately
known as
"The Pit."*

*The six operating rooms and the
laboratory were equipped with the
latest in medical technology.*

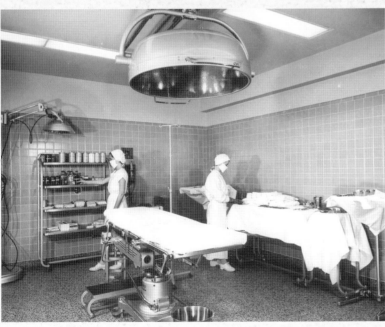

The First Patient

On June 23, 1952 — eight days after the balloons had floated away from the hot and historic dedication ceremony — Mayor Watkins Overton, with about 300 people present, officially opened the hospital doors to patients. Three-year-old Patty Lynn Bowden of Philadelphia, Mississippi was admitted as the first patient to Le Bonheur Children's Hospital. Patty was treated for nephrosis, a kidney disorder. One week later, on June 30, the hospital's first surgical procedure was performed, a case from the Crippled Children's Hospital. In December, the hospital's first major cardiovascular surgery was performed on thirteen-year-old Jerry Smith of Booneville, Mississippi.

The hospital's first chief administrator was Freeman E. May. Miss Dorothy Akes was the operating room superintendent and Miss Rose Turner was the supervisor of nurses. The annual operating budget was $600,000, with ten percent budgeted for charity care.

The hospital's first Chief of Staff was Dr. Tom Mitchell, head of the Division of Pediatrics at the University of Tennessee. By 1952, he had been practicing pediatrics in Memphis for 34 years, and he had developed a national reputation as an authority on child care. Unfortunately, Dr. Mitchell's appointment seemed to confirm the fears of the community's private pediatricians that Le Bonheur would be controlled by the University, and the hospital found that it still faced somewhat of an uphill battle to win the confidence of "town" as well as "gown."

The first physician to occupy an office at Le Bonheur was Dr. Ray N. Paul, a general pediatrician who would later specialize in pediatric cardiology. "I moved into the hospital in February 1952," recalls Dr. Paul, "about four months before the hospital was officially opened. They built a special staircase, sidewalk, and finished a hallway up to my office, which was on the second floor, so that I could start to practice. The rest of the hospital was just a shell, concrete pillars and concrete floors, nothing finished at all."

"At that time, remembers Dr. Paul, "we were getting $3 for an office visit and $5 for a house call."

Mr. Freeman May, Le Bonheur's first chief administrator.

The hospital's first patient was three-year-old Patty Lynn Bowden of Philadelphia, Mississippi.

By the end of 1952, the hospital had had 851 admissions and 621 surgical procedures. The average daily patient load for these first six months was 30, but by January 1953 there was already an average of 62 patients in the hospital each day. In 1953, the first full year of operations, there were 3,205 admissions and 1,615 surgical procedures.

Le Bonheur was the first hospital in Tennessee designed and built for children, but that was only the beginning of its list of "firsts." In 1954, Dr. Albert Jones established the state's first Poison Center at Le Bonheur. That same year, Miss Mary Kathryn Taylor became the first Medical Social Worker in any private hospital in Memphis, and Dr. Chet Lloyd set up practice in Le Bonheur as the region's first pediatric dentist. In 1957, Le Bonheur became the first hospital in Memphis to open an intensive care unit. That same year, it opened the city's first Mental Retardation Clinic for children. In 1958, Dr. Guinn Robbins was the first surgeon in Memphis to use a heart-lung machine during open-heart surgery. This tradition of remaining on the cutting edge of healthcare continues today.

By the time the Le Bonheur Club was hosting an open house to celebrate the hospital's fifth anniversary in 1957, construction had already begun on a Recovery Room and fourth floor ward facilities. The celebration and the construction were overseen by the hospital's second administrator, Adalbert G. Dierks, who had taken the reins on May 17, 1954, after Freeman May left to head the Baptist Hospital in Alexandria, Louisiana.

As was envisioned in Dr. Barton Etter's speech to the Le Bonheur Club in 1947, a key aspect of the hospital was that it served as a center for teaching pediatric medicine. From its opening to the present day, Le Bonheur has been closely affiliated with the University of Tennessee Department of Pediatrics and has served as the medical school's pediatric training ground for medical students, residents, and fellows. The relationship allows the University to provide a world-class pediatric medical education with hands-on experience in virtually every pediatric subspecialty, while the hospital receives the expertise of world-renowned pediatric experts and the enthusiasm of an entire staff of pediatric residents.

The hospital's second administrator, Adalbert G. Dierks, took the reins on May 17, 1954.

Private pediatrician Charles Householder admitted the first patient to Le Bonheur in 1952.

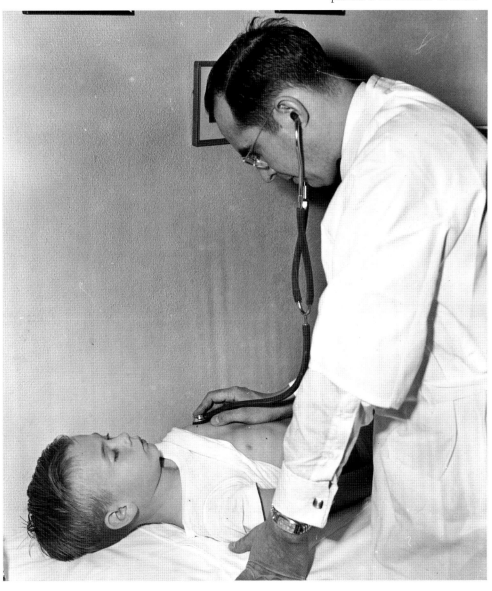

"Jacks-of-all-Trades"

One thing was apparent to anyone involved with the hospital in its early days: This was the Le Bonheur Club's hospital. The ladies of Le Bonheur appointed and served on the board of directors, but they also sewed clothes for the children, staffed the gift shop, and even ran the elevators. They kept The Bunny Room stocked with toys, some of which they made. In 1953, they contributed the equivalent of $30,000 in volunteer work, a significant sum in a time when hospital room rates were less than $20 a day. "Private rooms were under $20 a day," remembers James Aune, Le Bonheur's first comptroller. "I think semi-private was about $12.50 a day. The nursery area was around $6 a day."

"Sewing was one of the main activities," recalls Billie Ann Williams, 1976-77 Le Bonheur Club president, "and I enjoyed doing that because you got to know some of the other members well sewing together. And you felt like you were doing something worthwhile for the hospital — making toys, sheets, the children's gowns, which always had a cute, juvenile-type fabric that was fun to work with. Also I worked on the Snoopy Cart, which went from room to room and took crafts to the children, and we used to have a shift where you just visited the children and the parents, just knocking on the door and asking, 'Can I do anything for you today?'"

"You don't really think about parents not being able to leave their room when they have babies there, and how nice it is for someone to come to the door with a magazine or a cup of coffee," says Virginia Gibson, 1981-82 Club president.

"I worked behind the desk and we had the pneumatic tubes where they would fill prescriptions and shoot them up to the floors and then back to the pharmacy," recalls Gail French, Le Bonheur Club president 1980-81. "I would answer the phone, assist parents, and give them directions where to take the child. We were kind of jacks-of-all-trades, and then we had the Sunshine Girls and would sit in rooms with children. One of my experiences was sitting with a dying child, which was quite memorable."

"I became a member in the '60s and did Sunshine work at the hospital, which was working with patients," recalls Flo Hinson, Le Bonheur Club President 1975-76. "There was at that particular time a little burned girl there named Hattie Bell, and I read to her and she got to go home and it was a really amazing experience for me. It made me very grateful for my own healthy children."

"It was an organized bunch of volunteers," says founding board member Palmer Brown of the Le Bonheur Club ladies. "Some of them were as dedicated as any employee could have been." Pediatrician Price Stepp, M.D. agrees. "It was a very enthusiastic group," he says. "They were forward-thinking ladies, and they did a darn good job."

Nor did the members of the Club cease their legendary fundraising activities. In 1952 they conducted a special fundraising drive for the hospital's needs prior to its opening. In 1953 they sold Memphis State football tickets and Memphis auto tags and moved their medical clinics into the hospital. In 1954, the Club received *McCall's* magazine's national award for best monthly public service project.

Club members collect Christmas gifts for the patients of Le Bonheur in 1952. Pictured left to right are Mrs. Russ Pritchard, Mrs. E.T. Hutton, Mrs. J. Wells Hanley, Mrs. James A. Dew, and Mrs. Raymond Berson Frye.

The Sewing Room

The Le Bonheur Club began as a sewing club for orphaned children, so it's no surprise that The Sewing Room became a mainstay in the hospital. The ladies sewed hospital gowns, bed linens, and stuffed toys. The Sewing Room remained an important part of the hospital all the way into the 1980s, until synthetic materials and mass-market manufacturing methods made it cheaper to buy clothes than to make them.

Members of the Club at work in the original Sewing Room at the hospital's opening.

For many years, Mrs. Irene Martin Schaeffer was the matriarch of The Sewing Room, coordinating and supervising the volunteers.

The Sewing Room in the 1950s.

The Sewing Room in the Club's new suite following construction in the 1970s.

The Sewing Room in 1960.

"Everybody Knew Everybody"

But what people remember most about Le Bonheur in its early days was the relaxed and homey feeling made possible by the hospital's small size and specialized mission.

"Le Bonheur then was just a nice, friendly, small, quiet, gentle hospital," recalls Dr. J. T. Jabbour, Pediatric Neurologist. "When you walked in, after all, you walked right into a little diner. There was a little soda fountain-type diner. There was also a drug store, a gift shop, and a chapel, and then you walked back into the hospital."

"I came to Le Bonheur in 1952, October the 5th," says Bernice Warren, Chief Cook. "I started on a Saturday, washing dishes. I was here forty-one years and ten months before I retired. It was small and everybody knew everybody. Back in the fifties and sixties we knew everybody. We knew the nurses from the first floor on up to the fourth floor, the early shifts and the late. So that made it more like a family."

"It was a quaint little hospital that had the right feeling for pediatrics," says Dr. Earle Wrenn, who began his residency at Le Bonheur in 1954. "Everybody was a child-loving person, it seemed. Being quite small at that time, Le Bonheur was a very family-friendly sort of place. We used to all gather down in the lobby to watch the World Series on the TV. It was just a real close-knit outfit and a very pleasant place to work."

"There was a great camaraderie, at least at that time," agrees Dr. Ray Paul. "This was a meeting place for pediatricians. We really thought we were uptown at that time. Let's face it, we had the best of the equipment for that period."

"I was a medical student at the UT College of Medicine from 1952 to 1955, when Le Bonheur was a brand new hospital," recalled Dr. Robert Summitt when he was Dean of the UT College of Medicine. "I liked to come to Le Bonheur because their food was a lot better than the food at City Hospital. It was a well run, small children's hospital."

"I came here April 26, 1956," says Louise Jackson, who worked as a cook in the cafeteria. "I felt like you knew everybody by name and knew where everybody worked and knew where to find everybody. So, at that time, it was like a family; you knew everybody. You did — administration, president, and everybody. Knew them by name."

"I came to Le Bonheur in 1962," recalls Margie Whitney, Nursing Duty Administrator, now retired. "The hospital was extremely small, of course. The one thing that I remember is the warmth of all the areas of the hospital, whether it was in maintenance, surgery, nurses, physicians — everybody had that deep abiding wanting to do what was best for the children. I feel that we have continued with that feeling and that dedication."

"There was a little lady, a frail little lady by the name of Gladys Brown that worked in the gift shop," recalls Fred Nowak of his early days as assistant administrator, "and she was very dedicated to Le Bonheur. One day a person came in — with a weapon, by the way — and went to rob her, and she talked that person out of robbing the place because all the money that was being made there was going to be used to help support the children here. She gave him a five dollar bill and told him to leave and he did."

Top: The hospital's pharmacy originally doubled as a commercial drug store open to the public.

Bottom: Le Bonheur's first pharmacist, Max Denslow, RPh, serves a customer.

Originally, in keeping with common practice of the day, the hospital's cafeteria and drugstore were open to the general public, and were promoted with retail signs out on the street. "When I came to Le Bonheur, in '63, there were homes all around Le Bonheur, so we were delivering prescriptions to people's homes," says Bert Price, who still serves as director of the pharmacy. "The pharmacy was a very small portion of the back of the drug store. You would walk in and you would think you were in a regular drug store, Walgreens or Super D. We had toothpaste, cosmetics, magazines and, of course, we had a lot of toys."

While prescriptions were usually sent up to patient floors via dumbwaiter and pneumatic tube, says Price, there were times when doctors and nurses "would walk into the drug store, past the toys, past the magazines, past the toothpaste, and we would hand them the drugs." The pharmacy kept regular drug store hours, which in those days meant closing at 5 pm. The night nurse had access to a lock box where prescriptions were left for after hours, but if a new need arose, she would call a nearby adult hospital and send someone to pick it up. The next day, the Le Bonheur pharmacist would take the drugs over to reimburse the other hospital.

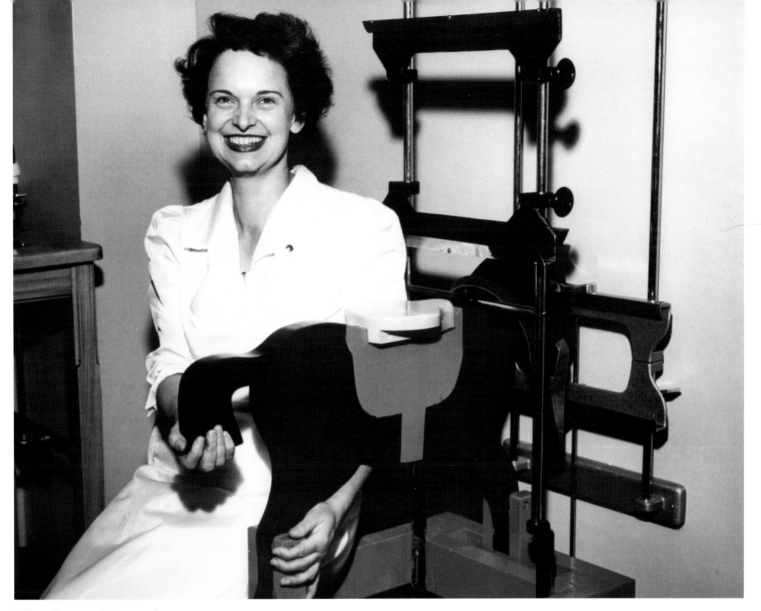

The Second Decade

In the 1960s, Le Bonheur Children's Hospital continued to establish its reputation as the preferred facility for pediatric care in the Mid-South. In 1960, a cardiovascular unit was established with funds donated by Mr. and Mrs. J. Everett Pidgeon. In 1961, with the help of $252,323 from the Hartford Foundation, research was started on the development of a miniature artificial kidney designed especially for children and infants.

During this time, Le Bonheur's chief radiologic technologist, Jalmer Pigg, was searching for a solution to the challenge of getting clear x-rays of squirming kids. Working at his home, he fashioned a metal frame with two plexiglass shields to hold children in place. He patented his invention as the "Pigg-O-Stat." The device was written up in medical journals and was soon in use in hospitals around the world. The Pigg-O-Stat continues to be used to the present day, and it is still marketed under its original name.

St. Jude Children's Research Hospital opened its doors in 1962 as a pediatric oncologic research center. The hospital soon gained international fame, with patients coming from all over the United States and around the world. While St. Jude looms large in the Memphis medical community, it should be pointed out that it is not in direct competition with Le Bonheur when it comes to clinical care and medical services. In fact, St. Jude patients who develop other medical problems as a result of their cancer are routinely treated at Le Bonheur.

Kid-friendly ideas at Le Bonheur included a riding horse to keep children occupied during chest x-rays.

The hospital's third president, Donald C. McGrath, Served from 1964 to 1968.

Charles William Bradley served as Le Bonheur's president for nine years from 1968 to 1977, making him the hospital's second longest-serving administrator

In 1963, Le Bonheur became the first hospital in Memphis to use "ultra-micro" techniques for blood studies, which allowed doctors to run a battery of tests on only a few drops of blood. Such technology was not merely a new convenience, but a lifesaving capability for premature babies with no more than a pint of blood in their bodies.

Of course, the Le Bonheur Club continued to support the hospital in a variety of ways throughout 1960s. In 1962, they ended their MSU football ticket project in favor of the more popular Gold Tag sale, which would go on to become the Club's longest running fundraising project. In 1963, the Club established the "Sunshine Girls" to provide personal service to patients and families. In 1964, they supervised the hospital's first remodeling.

The hospital's third administrator, Donald C. McGrath, served from January 1964 until March 1968. In April 1968, Bill Bradley became the hospital's fourth administrator. He would serve for exactly nine years.

Also in 1968, Memphis' first comprehensive children's orthopedic service was established at Le Bonheur. Before that, pediatric orthopedic surgery had been taught in various hospitals around the city, but no one hospital had enough cases to form a good program. With the cooperation of the city's orthopedic surgeons, one floor of Le Bonheur became the main site of service and teaching for children with diseases of the bones and joints.

In 1969, through a substantial contribution from Raymond C. Firestone, the hospital opened the Firestone Children's Outpatient Center, with clinics for muscular dystrophy and neuromuscular problems, rheumatoid arthritis, hemophilia, and cystic fibrosis (the only cystic fibrosis clinic in the state at the time). Mr. and Mrs. James D. Bryan of Westpoint, MS founded the Susan Barlow Bryan Research and Education Fund in honor of their daughter, who had been a patient.

A new prayer room was constructed in 1969, and the Children and Youth Project moved its headquarters into Le Bonheur. A comprehensive health program for children from low-income families in North Memphis, this program provided preventive and regular care for more than 4,500 children.

Throughout the 1960s, utilization rates at Le Bonheur continued to climb. From 1967 to 1968, for example, average daily admissions rose from 13.8 to 14.9, the average length of stay rose from 3.1 to 4.6 days, total patient days per month rose from 1385 to 1675, and total surgical procedures per month rose from 236 to 259.

Back in 1953, the hospital's first full year of operation, the Radiology Department had performed 3,631 procedures. In 1968, 11,437 procedures were performed. In 1953, there had been a total of 3,205 admissions and 1,615 surgical procedures performed. By 1969, annual admissions had nearly doubled to 5,942, while surgical procedures had nearly tripled to 3,664. In the seventeen years of the hospital's operation, 89,662 children had been admitted, 46,359 surgical procedures had been performed, and almost 5,000 medical students and 200 pediatric residents had been trained at Le Bonheur.

Famous Faces at Le Bonheur

From its earliest days, Le Bonheur has attracted celebrities who have given unselfishly of their time to help ease the pain of hospitalized children. In the 50s and 60s, visiting celebrities ranged from television stars to the mayor of Memphis.

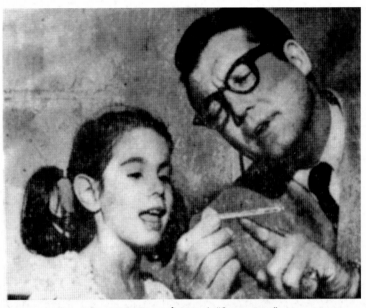

George Reeves, television's "Superman."

Singing cowboy Roy Rogers

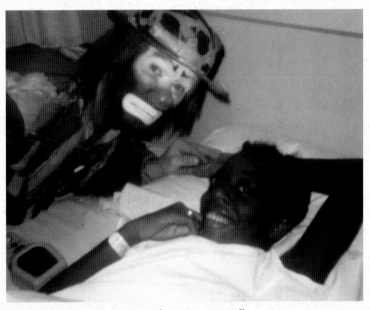

Famous clown Emmett Kelley

Memphis Mayor Henry Loeb

Duncan Renaldo, television's "The Cisco Kid"

Le Bonheur Doctors:
The First Twenty Years

The 1969 medical staff officers were (left to right) Dr. Emmett Bell, Secretary; Dr. R. N. Paul, Chief of Staff; Dr. William Threlkeld, Chief of Medicine; Dr. Albert Jones, Vice President; and Dr. Earle Wrenn, Chief of Surgery.

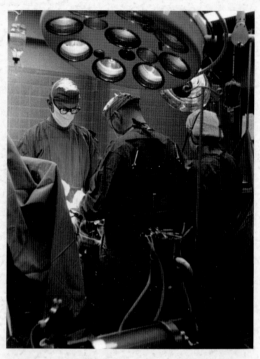

Dr. Guinn Robbins (left) and Dr. Robert G. Allen perform heart surgery in April 1959, assisted by Laura MacDougal, R.N.

Dr. Ray Paul joined the medical staff in 1952 and was the first to open an office in the hospital. A general pediatrician, he later specialized in pediatric cardiology.

Dr. Emmett Bell, pediatric cardiologist, joined the Le Bonheur medical staff in 1957.

Dr. Sid Wilroy, pediatric genetics, joined the medical staff in 1965.

Pediatric nephrologist Shane Roy, M.D. joined the medical staff in 1966.

Dr. Pat Wall, general pediatrics, joined the medical staff in 1968.

Dr. Jourdan Roane, pediatric allergy & immunology, joined the medical staff in 1968.

Dr. Phil George, pediatric pulmonology, joined the medical staff in 1969.

Dr. Al Camacho, pediatric endocrinology, joined the medical staff in 1965.

Left: The medical staff gathers in the auditorium for weekly Grand Rounds.

Below: Dr. Gene Lawyer addresses the group.

The 1964 Le Bonheur Pediatric Residents and the UT Professors of Pediatrics

First row, left to right: Aram Hanissian, Alvaro Camacho, Lloyd Crawford, Atrero Abai, James Hughes, James Ettledorf, James Sweeney, Robert Summitt, Lorin Aniger. Second row: Gene Lawyer, Bob Tiony, Jack Roane, Gary Edwards, John McEachin, Darrell Johnson, Frayser Triplett, Sid Wilroy, Charlie Fitch, Stanley Crawford. Third row: John Rocha, unidentified, John Pender, unidentified, unidentified, Louis Navano, unidentified, Bill Young, Shane Roy, Sergio DeLammareno, Kathryn Jared. Fourth row: George Brasher, John Dyer, Charlie Roper, unidentified.

Out of Disappointment. . .
A Plan Is Born

When Le Bonheur Children's Hospital opened in 1952, its facility and equipment were so modern that it won national recognition. But in healthcare, what is state-of-the-art today can become outmoded tomorrow. Throughout its fifty years of existence, Le Bonheur has witnessed significant developments in medical technology, an increased specialization among healthcare professionals, and a steadily growing population in the Memphis area. The result? A seemingly never-ending series of modernizations, remodelings, and expansions.

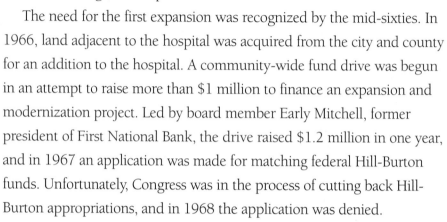

The need for the first expansion was recognized by the mid-sixties. In 1966, land adjacent to the hospital was acquired from the city and county for an addition to the hospital. A community-wide fund drive was begun in an attempt to raise more than $1 million to finance an expansion and modernization project. Led by board member Early Mitchell, former president of First National Bank, the drive raised $1.2 million in one year, and in 1967 an application was made for matching federal Hill-Burton funds. Unfortunately, Congress was in the process of cutting back Hill-Burton appropriations, and in 1968 the application was denied.

Although the application was turned down, federal officials did point out that funds were available to help communities implement new federal planning guidelines for avoiding the duplication of healthcare services. Memphis could achieve this goal by merging all or most pediatric services into one institution. The core of the plan that emerged was the consolidation of all the city's pediatric services into a new "Memphis Children's Medical Center." The site was to be across the street from Le Bonheur, where the Memphis Steam Laundry sat adjacent to the West Tennessee Tuberculosis Hospital. Le Bonheur's existing building would be purchased by the state and converted into a children's psychiatric facility. Services provided by Le Bonheur, the University of Tennessee, the City of Memphis hospitals, Les Passees Rehabilitation Center, and other organizations serving children would be incorporated into the grand plan. Memphis would have one of the finest children's medical centers in the United States, if not the world.

Application was made by Le Bonheur and the University of Tennessee for funding through the Bureau of Health Manpower. Le Bonheur's board of directors authorized the drawing of architectural plans. Then things went wrong again. In 1969, federal cutbacks reduced funding for hospital construction, and no action was taken on the Memphis Children's Medical Center application.

Nevertheless, the groundwork for Le Bonheur's future had been laid. In the closing months of the decade, the plans for a children's medical center resulted in the first formal affiliation between Le Bonheur and the University of Tennessee. With this affiliation agreement in place, and with cooperation pledged by the rest of the medical community and children's service providers, Le Bonheur looked forward to the 1970s as a decade promising a new phase in its history. It would not be disappointed.

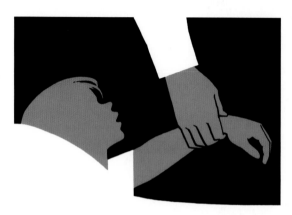

Le Bonheur's "Helping Hand" logo was created by artist Edgar Bailey for the cover of the 1966 fund drive brochure. On the facing page is a photo from that brochure.

Le Bonheur board member Early Mitchell, former president of First National Bank (later First Tennessee), led the fundraising campaign for the hospital's first expansion. While the campaign was successful, cutbacks in federal funds delayed the project until the early '70s.

CHAPTER THREE

Adolescence

The turbulence of the 1960s spilled over into the 1970s, and in the early part of the decade, the nation experienced continuing unrest, the end of the Vietnam War, the Watergate scandal, and the eventual resignation of a president. But at Le Bonheur, the focus, as always, was on taking care of children.

In 1970, the J. Everett Pidgeon, Jr. Memorial Loan Fund was established as a loan-grant fund for hospital in-service education. That same year, the hospital tried a short-lived experiment called the "Care-By-Parent Unit," in which parents cared for their children with minor illnesses who required hospitalization but no extensive nursing care. The Le Bonheur Club received the Margaret Forbes *Commercial Appeal* Service Award, and the Club's "Golden Girls" — a singing and dancing group — received the "key to the city" for helping to promote the city's sesquicentennial celebration.

In 1971, the Club established Le Bonheur Teens, made up of daughters of members, who took part in fundraising events and provided volunteer service.

In 1972, Le Bonheur celebrated its twentieth anniversary by adding physical therapy, psychological testing, and audiology and speech pathology. Governor Winfield Dunn was the principal speaker at the annual meeting of the hospital board. Le Bonheur was honored to be the only hospital in the United States to be visited by the world champion table tennis team of the People's Republic of China.

In 1973, a 16-year-old boy named Tommy Smith came to Le Bonheur with kidney problems. An anonymous Memphis businessman offered to pay Tommy's bill, which amounted to more than $3,500. The donor mentioned Tommy to a friend, Dr. J. R. Shelton, who was also thinking about making a donation to the hospital. Dr. and Mrs. Shelton gave $10,000 to establish the Sidney Shelton Hemo Dialysis Unit, which they named after their own healthy eight-year-old son. Le Bonheur's was the first pediatric kidney dialysis unit in the southeastern United States, and one of only five in the nation at that time.

Other donations poured in. The hospital's Medical Library was endowed by gifts from Mr. Graham Dudley and friends as a memorial to his wife, Harriet Dudley. Mr. and Mrs. Hall Jones, Sr., and Mr. and Mrs. Harry Phillips provided $150,000 in seed money for a special unit for comprehensive services for children with neurological and psychological problems. The remaining $1 million was raised through a fund drive, to which the city and county governments pledged $100,000 each.

Facing page: Early on, the little red wagon became the preferred method of transportation for Le Bonheur patients.

The Le Bonheur Club celebrated its 50th anniversary in January 1973 with a party and a $50,000 gift to the hospital building fund. In addition, the Club donated $83,000 to the Children's Fund, $5,000 for landscaping, $10,000 for Club Rooms, $20,000 to the endowment fund, and $40,000 to pay for charity care. By the end of the year, they had given an additional $50,000 gift to the building fund. In 1974, the Club gave 8,641 hours of volunteer service and $265,861 to the hospital. The Le Bonheur ladies also hired their first employee, an executive secretary who assisted with clerical work and coordinated volunteer services.

In 1973, former Club president Jane Doles Jones became the hospital's first female chairman of the board. She would go on to serve four consecutive terms, and in 1975 she would simultaneously serve as president of the National Association of Children's Hospitals and Related Institutions (NACHRI). Her involvement with NACHRI would help expand Le Bonheur's horizons by putting it more closely in contact with other children's hospitals around the country.

The Le Bonheur Club remained the organization of choice for young society women, and its officer elections and new member inductions were dutifully covered in the society pages. *The Commercial Appeal* ran editorials urging the public to take part in the Club's Gold Tag Sale, and the *Memphis Press-Scimitar* ran banners across the bottom of its pages that read "Buy a Bumper Sticker — Help LB Children's Hospital."

In 1974, a new major educational affiliation agreement was established between Le Bonheur and the Department of Pediatrics of the University of Tennessee. As a result, Le Bonheur officially became the principal pediatric teaching hospital of UT. A chaplain residency program was begun in cooperation with the University. Also, a new 10-bed unit was opened for metabolic and endocrine patients.

Above: Le Bonheur Club members Flo Gray and Florence Hays continue the tradition of taking the Library Cart to patient rooms.

Right: Another favorite was the Snoopy Cart, which brought games and arts & crafts to patients' rooms. Cartoonist Charles Schultz gave the hospital official permission to use images of the Peanuts gang in children's activities.

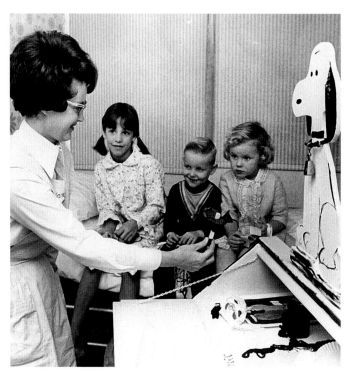

Under the name "Day Care," Le Bonheur helped pioneer outpatient surgery for minor procedures such as wart removal, dental rehabilitation, or cast changes. While same-day surgery was a radical move at the time, it provided obvious benefits by reducing costs, disrupting lives less, and reducing the stress that a hospital stay might bring to young patients. Over the following decades, with improved technology, same-day surgery would become the norm for a growing number of procedures.

Woman of the Hour

Jane Doles Jones served as Le Bonheur Club president from 1970-1971, a position that automatically placed her on the hospital's board. In 1973, she became the hospital's first female chairman of the board. She went on to serve four consecutive terms. In 1975, she simultaneously served as president of the National Association of Children's Hospitals and Related Institutions (NACHRI), which placed her on the national stage as an advocate for children's healthcare.

In 1969-70, Mrs. Jones (behind chair) was President-elect of the Le Bonheur Club. Also pictured are (left to right) Lucy Carrington Jones, President Ruth Crenshaw, Mary Lou Claxton, and Pat Moore.

Jane Jones chairs a Le Bonheur hospital board meeting, as she did for four consecutive years.

As president of the National Association of Children's Hospitals and Related Institutions, Mrs. Jones was invited to Washington, D.C. to address a congressional subcommittee on children's healthcare needs.

Mrs. Jones confers with Congressman Harold Ford, Sr. (right), whose district included Le Bonheur.

Seventies Smiles

Mrs. Leola Woods joined the Dietary Department on July 7, 1952. In 1973, she was selected by her peers as Employee of the Year.

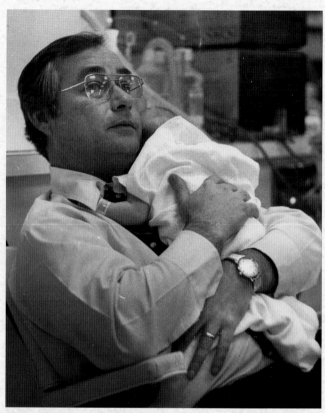

Hospital administrator Bill Bradley demonstrates the "TLC Machines"—rocking chairs provided in the Infant Care Unit.

Bert Price, Pharmacy Director, seen here in the mid-'70s, joined the Le Bonheur staff in 1963. At the hospital's 50th anniversary in 2002, he was preparing to celebrate his 40th year of service.

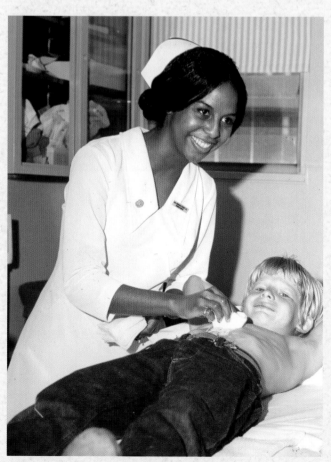

ER Nurse Gwen Bynote preps a young patient for tests.

3rd Floor Ward Clerk Clara Wolverton in 1976.

Personnel Dir. Francis Crabtree decorates the office Christmas tree with Mary Snipes.

Arthur Halle, Jr. served on Le Bonheur's board of directors from 1968 to 1982.

Don Currie, Materials Administrator, in 1976.

Mrs. Elma Jordan, Business Office Administrator, in 1974.

Alice Cantrell, Director of the Operating Room.

Jim Overall, Director of Purchasing.

Doug Platt, Director of Engineering, in 1974.

Carol Knodel, Anesthesiology Administrator.

Art therapy has always been an important tool for maintaining patient morale at Le Bonheur.

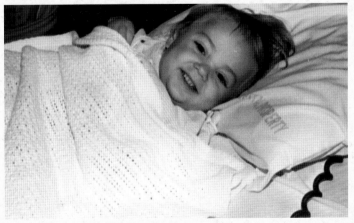

A young dialysis patient smiles in the new Sidney Shelton Hemo Dialysis Unit, the first pediatric kidney dialysis unit in the southeastern United States.

When the 1970s began, the hospital's telephone operator was still using the original plug-style switchboard, and the hospital's emergency generator was an old hand-cranked Model-T engine.

Memphis architect J. Wise Smith was hired to take Le Bonheur into a new era.

Facing page: Land is cleared to the east of Le Bonheur for the hospital's first addition.

Phase One

The cutback in federal funds in 1969 had formed a roadblock to Le Bonheur's plans to move into a new, larger facility that would serve as a comprehensive pediatric medical center for Memphis and the Mid-South. As a result, Le Bonheur entered its third decade the same small, quiet hospital it had always been. "I started residency at Le Bonheur in the summer of 1970," says private pediatrician Bob Riikola, M.D. "Le Bonheur was quite a bit different then as compared to now. I mean dramatically different. The emergency room facility, which is sort of a dramatic, busy, interesting, vibrant place now, was one or two rooms on the first floor of the admissions area. A patient would drop in occasionally from time to time."

A homey atmosphere and personal attention were traditions at Le Bonheur, but so was a commitment to stay on the cutting edge of pediatric healthcare. By the beginning of the 1970s, it was clear that the existing facility could not accommodate the equipment and personnel necessary to meet that goal. "The emergency generator was an old Ford T-model engine with a hand clutch," says architect J. Wise Smith (no relation to the hospital's original architect, J. Frazer Smith). "It would crank automatically, but it was just a wing and a prayer once it was running." In the dawning age of telecommunications, the hospital's telephone operator was still using the same plug-style switchboard, and the pneumatic tube system still lined the walls.

In 1970, Le Bonheur and the University of Tennessee began working on a backup plan — a scaled-down approach that would establish a children's medical center on Le Bonheur's present site, with the existing hospital as the core unit. The hospital's board commissioned the drawing of architectural plans in phases, for a series of construction projects. The final goal was a facility that would accommodate 233 beds, along with ancillary areas capable of providing services for the pediatric inpatient and outpatient loads of both Le Bonheur and the City of Memphis Hospital.

Construction was approved for the first phase of the children's medical center, and the groundbreaking ceremony took place in December 1971. While work was going on, the hospital paid $425,000 for a nearly two-acre tract of land fronting Dunlap directly across from the hospital, to be used for additional parking.

At a final cost of $5.4 million, the first phase of Le Bonheur's incremental expansion added a new patient wing that increased Le Bonheur's bed number from 89 to 140. Two new floors added 10,000 square feet to the doctor's wing. The expansion also added eight new operating rooms, a dialysis unit, and an ICU for children under the age of two called the Pediatric Acute Observation Unit. The Le Bonheur Club's new suite included a sewing room, a library/crafts room, and a club lounge. Renovations were made to the original structure. In cooperation with the Memphis and Shelby County Mental Health Center, an acute, short-term, 10-bed inpatient mental health unit was opened for children with emotional problems.

First Growth

Le Bonheur's first major addition increased the number of patient beds from 89 to 140 and doubled the size of the Doctor's Wing. At the dedication ceremony, officials pronounced the hospital "past its childhood and into its adolescence." An even greater expansion would begin just a few years later.

The architectural rendering (top) and model (above) show the new three-story patient wing on the right, the new main entrance in the center, and the hospital's first public parking lot. Both images are looking northwest from Adams Avenue.

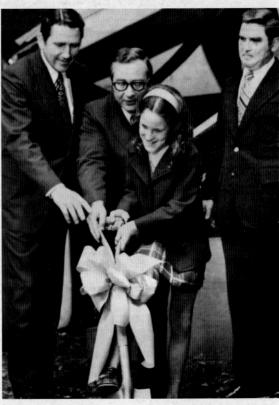

The groundbreaking ceremony took place in December 1971, using the same spade employed twenty years earlier to begin the original construction. Pictured are Tennessee Governor Winfield Dunn (left), Le Bonheur Administrator Charles W. Bradley, Hospital Board President W. H. Rachaels, M.D., and Dr. Rachaels' daughter Holly.

Top: The new patient wing stands proudly in fulfillment of the architect's vision.

Above: A fountain that greeted visitors at the hospital's new main entrance became even more delightful when it froze over one cold winter.

Left: The child-friendly artwork above the main entrance gave birth to the hospital's first official mascot, "Scooter."

The dedication ceremony for the new wing was held on Mother's Day, May 13, 1974. In keeping with tradition, a large gathering of balloons lifted a wooden key into the sky. *The Commercial Appeal* reported that "several hundred persons gathered on the hospital's front drive to hear officials proclaim the hospital 'past its childhood and into its adolescence.'"

Of course, adolescence can be a time of both triumph and tears, frustrations and growth spurts, and, most of all, rapid and profound changes. That Le Bonheur's adolescence would be no different was already being foreshadowed in a report commissioned about the time that the dedication ceremony was taking place.

The Hamilton Report

In 1974, Le Bonheur engaged James A. Hamilton Associates, a Minneapolis-based hospital consulting firm, to conduct an in-depth study that would aid the hospital in its long-term planning. In June 1975, the firm issued its two-pound, 173-page report entitled "The Le Bonheur Plan." This plan was adopted by the board of directors, and it guided the next decade's growth and development.

Looking back on the plan in 1980, hospital president Eugene K. Cashman, Jr. said, "The Le Bonheur Plan has been followed with remarkable faithfulness. Its projections have been remarkably accurate. Viewed from the perspective of today, these statements of five years ago turned out to be quite prophetic."

The report's opening statements — summarizing Le Bonheur's future role and what it would take to assume that role — demonstrate the increasing complexity and sophistication of healthcare:

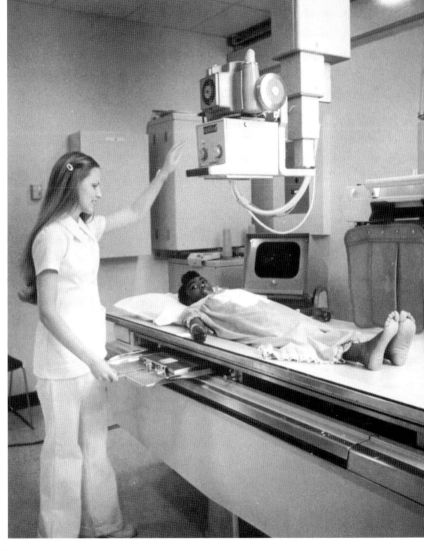

- *Becoming a children's medical center will involve a significant role change, accompanied by tremendous responsibilities, for the Board of Directors.*
- *Costs related to standards of excellence, technological advancements, and teaching will be extremely high.*
- *Organizational complexities with the University will continue to multiply and require ongoing philosophical and policy clarification in terms of programs, planning, and budget.*
- *Contractual arrangements negotiated with City-County government will necessitate new levels of public accountability and fiduciary expertise.*
- *Increased public relations and public information efforts will subject the Hospital and its staff to added visibility and scrutiny.*
- *Sensitive medical staff relationships with private practitioners and faculty will increase in volume and complication.*
- *A changing patient mix will necessitate greater understanding of interpersonal feelings.*
- *Once the Hospital assumes Medical Center status, there will exist a compelling need for perpetual, high-quality, informed leadership and direction by the Board of Directors.*

The proposed plan took into account the shared desire to consolidate all or most of the community's pediatric healthcare services into a single institution. In order to achieve this goal, said the report, Le Bonheur should seek to:

- *Be a component in a multi-institutional medical center setting.*
- *Serve as backup for the region's physicians and hospitals with sophisticated secondary and tertiary specialty programs and services.*
- *Offer complete general and specialty services — treat the most complex and the routine.*

The Children's Outpatient Clinic was a small part of the hospital in the early '70s. Over the following decade, as predicted by the Hamilton Report, outpatient subspecialty care would grow to become a significant portion of the hospital's services.

• In the new role of both specialty-referral center and community pediatric medical resource, allocate facilities to primary, secondary, and tertiary services.

• Be large enough in personnel, equipment, facilities, and funds to obtain the volumes necessary for setting and maintaining standards of medical excellence.

• Treat all patients with the same high quality care.

• Emphasize subspecialty clinical services to meet referral needs.

• Provide critical care, close observation, and maintenance observation care.

The Hamilton Report correctly saw outpatient care as an important new aspect of healthcare, stating that it should:

• Receive greater emphasis and resources.

• Be developed offsite as well as onsite.

• Meet the criteria of patient care that guide private office practitioners.

• Include encouragement of the development of ambulatory care professionals.

• Be open to all.

• Include primary care or walk-in office suites.

Other non-inpatient services that should be developed included:

• One-day surgery

• Preadmission diagnostic workups

• Ambulatory care followups

• Home care services

- *Observation units*
- *Backup programs for neighborhood clinics, physicians, schools, community hospitals, etc., to complement existing services.*
- *Logistical support, including transportation, computer, and telemetry.*

As for the relationship between Le Bonheur and the University of Tennessee, Le Bonheur should:

- *Consolidate with UT for pediatric research and education, but keep the hospital's primary focus on patient care.*
- *Have a tight affiliation agreement, but maintain independence in programs and services to be more competitive with other hospitals.*
- *Expect increasingly complex relationships with UT.*

In the area of medical education, said the report, Le Bonheur should:

- *Have a major responsibility for pediatric clinical education of medical, nursing, dental, and other allied health personnel in levels including undergraduate, graduate, post-graduate, and continuing education.*
- *Provide pediatric clinical training opportunities for other area colleges, universities, and hospitals.*
- *Share responsibility of developing child care personnel for the city, the region, and the nation.*
- *Plan significant increases in residents volumes, most notably in pediatrics, but also in pediatric subspecialties and ancillary services.*

And finally, in the area of research, Le Bonheur must:

- *Expand research in cooperation with UT and others to improve patient care and education programs and to promote basic and applied medical science.*
- *Recognize that basic science should remain a primary role of UT, but the Hospital program should not be limited to clinical medicine — it should investigate healthcare delivery systems, measurements of patient care, incentives for operational improvements, and reimbursement mechanisms.*
- *Recognize that clinical research should be a principal undertaking of the Department of Pediatrics, with some joint opportunities for the private staff and house staff.*

The Hamilton Report made one thing clear: As in so many areas of American society, the simple days of the past were ending. Just as Le Bonheur's cozy atmosphere had been compromised by its expansion, the days when a volunteer women's organization could run the hospital from the board room to the gift shop were coming to an end. As Flo Hinson, 1975-76 Le Bonheur Club president, puts it, "The Le Bonheur Club certainly was becoming aware that we were not going to be able to forever fulfill the needs of the hospital."

Sentimental Journey

In 1976, community activist Pat Plemons created the "Sentimental Journeys," a nostalgic train ride behind an old-timey steam locomotive, with proceeds going to Le Bonheur. The excursion raised more than $10,000 each year for the hospital.

In 1984, Pat was awarded Le Bonheur's Concern for Children Award. Former recipient Father Don Mowery (left) presented the award.

Pat dubbed his train "The Memphis Special."

The Arrival of Griffith, The Closing of Tobey

In 1976, one aspect of the Hamilton Report came to fruition that symbolized an important break from the past. As mentioned in The Le Bonheur Plan, the consolidation of pediatric services into a children's medical center at Le Bonheur necessarily meant bringing in the community's indigent patients. As a private hospital, Le Bonheur had always catered mainly to private patients, while those who couldn't afford to pay for their healthcare went to the pediatric unit of the city's Frank T. Tobey Memorial Hospital. In practice, this meant that Le Bonheur served mainly white children, while patients at Tobey were overwhelmingly children of color.

Le Bonheur had committed to the consolidation of these two programs in its 1970 architectural plans, but it had not taken place when Dr. James G. Hughes, Le Bonheur's medical director, resigned his post in 1975 to start the Center for Children in Crisis. In July 1976, Dr. John F. Griffith was named as his successor. As a Canadian, Dr. Griffith did not have the patience of many Southerners for a slow end to segregation. "When John Griffith came, he did some good things," says Dr. Robert Summitt, Dean of the UT College of Medicine. "One of his top priorities was for the Tobey Hospital to be closed and for the county to provide funding for the care of its medically indigent patients at Le Bonheur."

"I was assured we were going to consolidate both of the hospitals in time — a year or two or three," says Dr. Griffith. "I never would have come here unless there was an effort to put all children into one sort of facility, because children are children, after all. Frankly, soon after I arrived it moved much further up on my agenda. There was a sort of different standard of care between one hospital and the other. [Administrator] Bill Bradley, [Board Chairman] Jane Jones and others, we just moved the timetable ahead significantly. Within six months we basically had closed the Tobey Hospital and moved the patients over to Le Bonheur into a makeshift sort of ward that was constructed almost overnight."

"The children were moved, Tobey was torn down, and what I would call the modern era of Le Bonheur was really born," says UT Chancellor Bill Rice. "In the 1970s, Le Bonheur was a much smaller place than it is now — not, of course, nearly as attractive as it is today. I think it had an excellent reputation even at that time, however, and we were quite pleased when all the consolidation took place and the hospital began a growth phase."

"In the 1960s the relationship between Le Bonheur and UT was rather loose," explains Dr. Summitt, "because in those days the base of operations of the Department of Pediatrics was still in the Tobey Hospital, in what was then called either John Gaston or the City of Memphis Hospital. Whether we were faculty or residents, we sort of rotated between Tobey and Le Bonheur. The closing of Tobey changed the face of Le Bonheur considerably. That consolidated the Department of Pediatrics in Le Bonheur as it moved its headquarters out of Tobey over into the doctor's office building at Le Bonheur."

On February 1, 1977, Le Bonheur began admitting medical patients who previously would have gone to Tobey. The hospital experienced an increase of about forty patients per day, a significant load for a hospital that previously had an average daily census of around one hundred patients. Nevertheless, declared administrator Bill Bradley, "We will provide the same quality care for private and public patients and maintain our normal amount of free care."

One month later, on March 1, Le Bonheur began accepting pediatric emergency cases that had previously gone to the John Gaston unit of the City of Memphis Hospital. "This is part of our agreement with Shelby County to centralize pediatrics at Le Bonheur," said Bradley. "Outpatient pediatric services will remain at Gailor until we complete our building program."

"Patient visits will be about doubled, from 12,000 to 24,000 annually," predicted Dr. James S. Brown, Le Bonheur's director of Emergency Services. "House staff physicians will continue 24-hour coverage with one doctor present in ER late afternoon and through night hours." He added that the nursing staff would be increased, an orthopedic technician added, and surgery specialty residents made available.

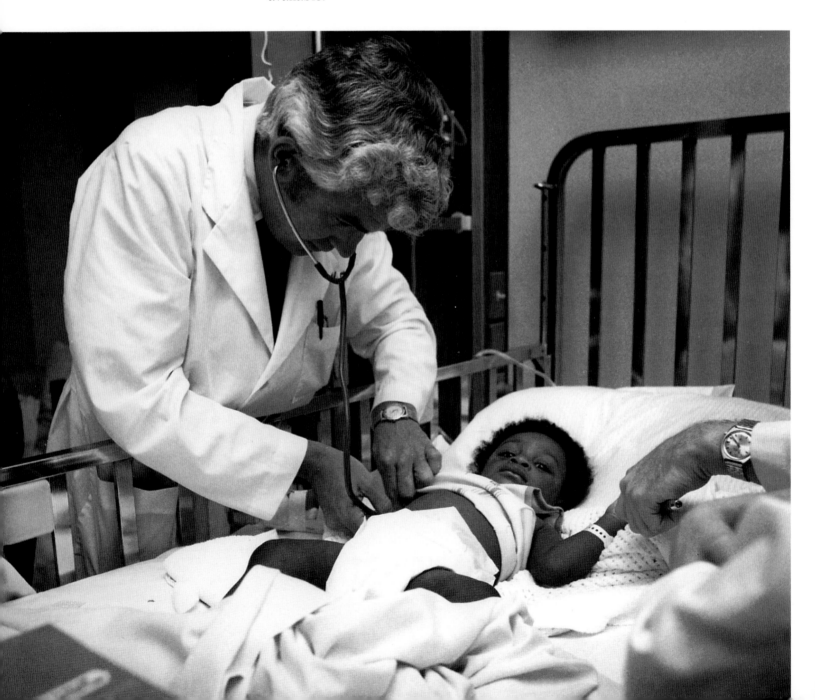

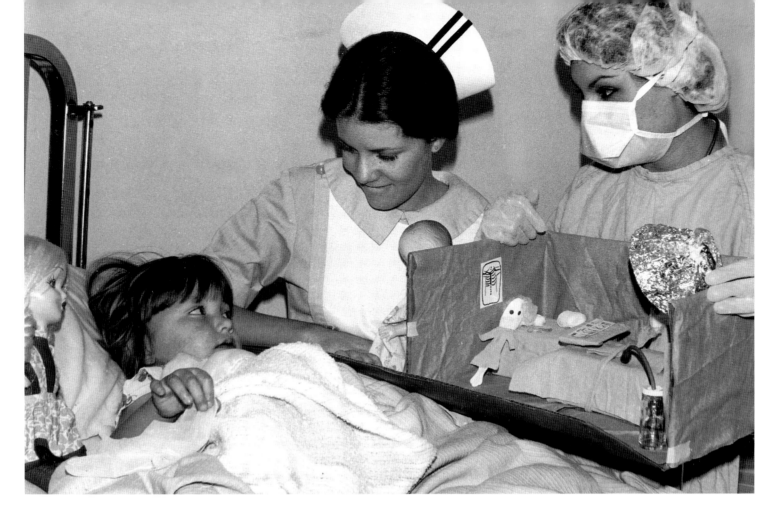

The Late Seventies

In 1975, Le Bonheur's national reputation was acknowledged when it was chosen to host the annual convention of the National Association of Children's Hospitals and Related Institutions. Representatives from 70 institutions attended. That same year, as suggested by the Hamilton Report, a new, closer affiliation agreement between Le Bonheur and UT was finalized.

Also in 1975, a closed-circuit television system was installed in the hospital through gifts from the Le Bonheur Club and American Women in Radio and Television. Still in use today, the system allows the hospital to broadcast important information to parents, and for employees to put on shows for the children. For example, every child in the hospital can simultaneously join in a game of Bingo, calling the in-house telephone number at the bottom of the screen when they fill a row. The first to call wins a prize that is then brought up to the child's room.

In 1976, the Le Bonheur Club initiated an information blitz, traveling to 30 towns in the surrounding area to give presentations about the hospital. The Club won the Distinguished Community Services Award of the Tennessee Hospital Association. In 1977, the Club gave $208,500 to the hospital.

Another phase of Le Bonheur's incremental expansion was completed on February 1, 1977 with the opening of a new 38-bed Infant Care Unit. The 3,500-square foot, ground-floor open ward featured a centralized nursing station for optimum patient observation and a four-patient isolation area. When fully staffed, the 50 nursing personnel provided a 6:1 patient to nurse ratio.

Beginning that same month, radiology services were made available 24 hours a day, seven days a week for the first time. Also for the first time, an operating room

Going to the hospital can be a frightening experience for young children who don't know what to expect. Le Bonheur alleviates these fears through programs using dolls, puppets, and other activities to explain to the child what will happen and why. For example, the nurse on the right is wearing a surgical outfit so the child will get used to seeing the mask and gloves.

In 1978, Mary Grogan was hired as Le Bonheur's first full-time Director of Volunteer Services.

Also in 1978, Susan Rambo (right) was hired as the first regional director for the TWIGS, neighborhood groups that do fundraising and volunteer work for the hospital.

was staffed for a new 3-11 shift, with personnel on-call and the room to be readied in less than 30 minutes. These changes were made partially to meet the increased demand after the closing of Tobey.

Le Bonheur already had eight subspecialty outpatient clinics in operation: cystic fibrosis, muscular dystrophy, rheumatoid arthritis, neuromotor, diabetes, nephrology, genetics, and endocrinology. In March 1977, these were joined by clinics for orthopedics and surgery. In July, the hospital opened the Center for Children in Crisis, a multidisciplinary center for abused or neglected children and their families. The next year, a seed-money grant from the Tennessee Lung Association was used to provide training for the director of the new Pediatric Pulmonary Center.

By the late seventies, Le Bonheur had served so many families and become such a presence in the community that people outside the Le Bonheur Club wanted to volunteer their time to help the children. In 1978, Mary Grogan was hired as the first full-time Volunteer Services Director. Five years later, in 1983, 8,419 volunteer shifts were worked, a total of 35,261 hours. Figured at minimum wage, the total annual contribution equaled nearly $120,000.

Also in 1978, Susan Rambo was hired as the first regional director of the TWIGS groups. Standing for "Together We Initiate Growth and Sharing," TWIGS are neighborhood groups that do volunteer work and fundraising. By Le Bonheur's 50th birthday in 2002, TWIGS chapters had raised nearly $3 million for the hospital. A favorite activity is the annual Festival of Trees, a holiday extravaganza started in the early 1980s. In 1990, the event was combined with the Enchanted Forest, a long-time Memphis tradition donated to the TWIGS by Goldsmith's when its downtown store closed. Today, the Enchanted Forest Festival of Trees attracts more than 70,000 people and raises more than $150,000 each year.

The hospital's silver anniversary celebration was held on June 15, 1977, where it was announced that more than 250,000 children had been treated by the hospital in its first 25 years. It was appropriate that 1977 marked a quarter century of Le Bonheur's service to the community, for it was in that year that the helm of the hospital was taken over by the man who was to serve as president of Le Bonheur longer than anyone else, and who was to guide the hospital through its most profound changes.

A Quarter Century of Caring

On June 15, 1977, Le Bonheur celebrated its Silver Anniversary with a birthday party on the West Patio. Guests of honor included Mrs. Elise Pritchard, the former Le Bonheur Club president who released the balloons at the hospital's opening in 1952, and two of the first ten patients admitted to the hospital. Entertainment included pony rides, wall painting, clowns, balloons, music, and a table-sized birthday cake.

Mrs. Jock Sanderson (center), who regularly portrayed Raggedy Ann for Le Bonheur patients, was joined by two clowns from Ringling Brothers and Barnum & Bailey Circus.

Le Bonheur Club president Billie Ann Williams (right) introduces Philip Perel, fifth patient admitted to Le Bonheur in 1952, and Mrs. Pat Hilderbrand Nichols, the hospital's seventh patient.

Famous Faces At Le Bonheur

In the 1970s, entertainers and athletes continued to take time to visit the children of Le Bonheur when passing through Memphis.

Top soul singer Isaac Hayes visits Le Bonheur's muscular dystrophy clinic to promote the 1973 Jerry Lewis Telethon. Here he greets patient Verleria Verges.

The world-champion table tennis team from the People's Republic of China visited Le Bonheur during their 1972 tour of America.

City Mayor Wyeth Chandler (left) and Shelby County Mayor Roy Nixon help Club member Barbara Denney promote a 1979 citywide paper drive to benefit Le Bonheur.

To children in 1970, there was no bigger star than Johnnie Whitaker, who played "Jody" on the popular television show "A Family Affair."

The Shrine Circus Clowns visit with 3-year-old Curtis Johnson of Steens, Mississippi in February 1972. (Staff photo from the Memphis Press-Scimitar)

Larry Finch, star basketball player (and later coach) for Memphis State University, autographs his photo for patients in 1972.

Golf legend Arnold Palmer gets a tour from Le Bonheur medical director Dr. John Griffith in 1979.

Lucy May, 1971 Cotton Carnival Queen

Facing page: Bob Hope shows his support thirty years after serving as master of ceremonies at the Le Bonheur Horse Show. His support would continue into the 1990s through his participation in the Children's Miracle Network Telethon.

In November 1977, 35-year-old Eugene K. Cashman, Jr. became Le Bonheur's fifth administrator. He would go on to serve longer than any other president, and he would lead Le Bonheur through its most profound changes.

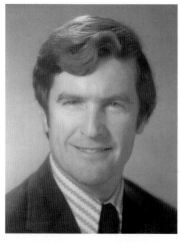

Le Bonheur board chairman Richard Trippeer, Jr., president of Union Planters Bank, played a personal role in recruiting Gene Cashman. Trippeer served on the hospital's board of directors for nine years and on the board of parent company Le Bonheur Health Systems, Inc. for thirteen years.

Under New Management

When Richard A. Trippeer, Jr. joined Le Bonheur's board of directors in 1973, he was an executive at Union Planters Bank, and he knew how to read a balance sheet. Along with other board members, he was concerned about the institution's solvency — especially given the massive construction projects underway. By the time he took over as chairman in 1977, there were real concerns.

"I found pretty early on in my chairmanship that the hospital was in real chaos,'" says Trippeer. "We were four or five months behind in paying our bills. We weren't receiving any collectibles. Admissions was just a mess. We had a construction project that was just not going well. The financial condition was pretty desperate."

Recognizing the chairman's desire to build a new leadership team, Administrator Bill Bradley submitted his resignation, announcing the end of his nine-year tenure on the day before the April groundbreaking for the final phase of the medical center construction. The search for a new hospital president began immediately.

"We hired a search firm and came up with a short list of four or five candidates," says Trippeer, "and very quickly worked it down to two candidates. One of the candidates was a very mature man, very conservatively dressed, probably in his 50s, a very traditional hospital-type administrator, and the other man was a guy that talked about 90 miles an hour and had more ideas than I could listen to or understand. He was about 35 years old. After quite a bit of deliberation we decided we would hire Gene Cashman, who was then an Associate Administrator at Children's Hospital National Medical Center in Washington, D.C."

Gene Cashman, who stood 5' 8" and had a boyish face that made him look even younger than he was, had his age against him. "He was younger than most boards at that time would consider," says Trippeer, "but he was so bright and had done so many of the things that we needed at the time. He had even played a role in a construction project at Washington, as I recall, so he had some construction experience and computer background. But it wasn't that easy a decision between those last two candidates, between Gene and the other candidate, because the other guy had a wonderful career and was 15 years older than Gene. He was just more mature. He had a longer record of achievement, so it wasn't a slam dunk-type of decision. It was a pretty gutsy decision, I think, that the Executive Committee and the board made to hire Gene."

A native of Savannah, Georgia and a graduate of Auburn University, Cashman was familiar with the ways of the South. Sallie Foster, who would be the new president's executive secretary, recalls the first time she spoke with Cashman on the telephone: "One of the things he said was that he and his family were so excited about coming to Memphis because they could get turnip greens and barbecue, because they could not get that in Washington. I thought, 'Hey, this guy is okay.'"

"When the decision was made to select Gene Cashman," recalls Fred Nowak, acting president during the search, "one of the board members said, 'He's either going to be the best thing or the worst thing that ever happened to this place.' He turned out to be the best thing."

Having decided that Gene Cashman was the man they wanted, the board tendered an offer that the search firm assured them was adequate. Cashman turned it down flat. The next morning, Trippeer flew to Washington to meet with him and discuss the situation. "We talked for about two hours, maybe," says Trippeer. "He talked about his vision for the future, healthcare in the world, children's healthcare, and I talked about what it would take to get him to come to Memphis, Tennessee and run Le Bonheur. In about two hours we shook hands. We had struck a deal." Within a month, Gene Cashman had moved to Memphis and taken over the reins of Le Bonheur Children's Hospital.

"Let me tell you," adds Trippeer, "when you carve my tombstone one day, I want you to put on it, 'Here lies Dick Trippeer. The most important thing he ever did in his business and community life was hire Gene Cashman to come to Le Bonheur.' Without a doubt, Gene saved this hospital and has made a great name for himself, made a great reputation for the hospital and my part in it will always be as important as anything I've ever done."

Upon his arrival on November 1, 1977, the new president discovered just what a challenge he had ahead of him. The hospital was experiencing a 78% turnover rate in its nursing staff. Employee morale was low. The medical staff and the University had developed an adversarial relationship. Surveys showed that there was little public awareness of what Le Bonheur was and what it did. Nothing was being done to draw in the suburban population that was rapidly shifting eastward. The latest review by the Joint Commission on Accreditation of Healthcare Organizations (JCAHO) had found 125 deficiencies.

Gene Cashman holds patient Rebecca Lundy of Wynne, Arkansas in a photo published in the February 1, 1978 issue of The Progress, *Rebecca's hometown newspaper. They are joined by Mrs. William Harris (left) and Mrs. Albert Harvey, co-chairmen of the Le Bonheur Club's annual Gold Tag bumper sticker sale.*

Most frightening, however, was the financial situation. Not long before, the hospital that was in the middle of a multi-million dollar expansion had been forced to borrow $200,000 just to meet payroll. In addition, the hospital had an accounts payable backlog of $207,000. There was no current audited financial statement, threatening the status of the bond issue that was funding the new expansion.

Recalls former board chairman Jane Jones, "We had town and gown problems. We had money problems. We had the problem of convincing the community that this was a worthwhile place for them to put their money. There were a lot of problems we had in those days. Largely, I think, they were psychological as well as physical problems."

Cashman lost no time in setting things right. In his first month, he established an Accounts Receivable Work Program to analyze the entire flow of charges throughout the hospital, including a review of all internal procedures in the Business Office. The program resulted in improved documentation, the development of quality control mechanisms, a 33% reduction in discharge billing time, and a computerized reclassification of all accounts receivable. For the first time, accounts were separated into inpatient and outpatient accounts, and collection efforts on bad debts were begun. Ernst & Whinney was hired as the hospital's audit firm, and in January 1978, three months after Cashman's arrival, revised data was submitted to establish the hospital's position in repaying its $15 million bond.

Cost-cutting efforts and new revenue sources were also analyzed. The hospital severed its management contracts for its parking lots and in-room television sets and began managing these services directly, recapturing the revenue from these highly profitable services. The employee insurance program was revised to increase employee cost participation in keeping with industry standards.

"When I approached Le Bonheur, I found that we had a lot of great people," says Cashman. "I just pulled them all together and said, 'This is something we can do.' Everybody took a major part. We put our heads together and started working on a system of priorities and assignment of duties and responsibilities. We made up a list of things that would have to be corrected and

The new president meets with Medical Director John Griffith, M.D.

Gene Cashman (left) accepts a donation from Frank McQuire of Federal Express.

went around every single day and checked every area that was on the list. We asked
for accountability. We got results and straightened out the problems."

The efforts paid off. Amazingly, less than six months after Cashman's arrival, all
accounts payable and all bank notes were
current. By the end of 1978, the hospital was
showing a surplus of nearly $1 million, and
by 1981, annual revenue exceeded expenses
by almost $3 million. In 1982, total patient
revenue was almost nine times greater than
in 1977. By 1983, the hospital was awarded
an A+ bond rating.

As soon as efforts were in motion to avert
a financial crisis, Cashman turned to more
proactive matters. A hospital is only as good
as its people, and the morale among the
medical and support staffs of Le Bonheur was
at an all-time low. Cashman knew that he
had to win over three important groups: the
medical staff, the nursing staff, and the
hospital personnel.

*Less than six months after Gene
Cashman's arrival, the hospital was
once again current on all bank notes and
accounts payable. Here he celebrates with
comptroller James Aune and Business
Office director Mary Caldwell.*

Two months after his arrival, in January 1978, Cashman held a planning retreat
for the board of directors and the medical staff. A "Medical Staff Strength and
Weakness Study and Response" was commissioned, and the medical staff was
realigned. Division chiefs were established and the residency programs for
Le Bonheur, St. Jude, and UT were
integrated. Physician education was
upgraded and a physician recruitment
program was initiated.

The head of nursing services was elevated
to vice-president status, and Jennifer Jenkins
was hired from Knoxville Children's Hospital
to run the department. "When I arrived,"
says Jenkins, "at least half the nursing
positions were vacant. We lost about 60% of
all new graduates we hired within their first
year. There was not a good relationship
between nursing and medicine and certainly
not between nursing and administration.
Morale was terrible."

Jenkins moved to decentralize the
decision-making authority in the department, introducing new concepts such as
"shared governance," which gave individual nursing units input into decisions
affecting them, and "primary nursing," in which each patient had a single nurse
assigned to coordinate his or her care. "We were probably one of the first hospitals in

*A Le Bonheur tradition: Every
employee receives a frozen turkey just
before the Thanksgiving break. Here
Gene Cashman presents a turkey to
Dixie Fleck, RN.*

ANNOUNCING

TWIGS
of
Le Bonheur Children's
Medical Center, Inc.

FUND RAISING TOTAL
$14,000

amount represents money raised
by 16 TWIG groups since 1978.

the country to implement primary nursing and shared governance into a single cohesive professional practice model," Jenkins says. "We published articles on it and got some national recognition for it, and that was real positive for the staff."

A series of leadership development classes helped give the nursing staff the confidence they needed to take on more authority. Additionally, a nursing internship program was instituted. A full-time nurse recruiter was hired, and the hospital began to recruit nationally for the first time.

For hospital personnel, both medical and non-medical, Cashman moved to upgrade and systemize human resource procedures. Detailed, individual job descriptions for each position were created, along with standards of performance that removed the subjectivity from yearly evaluations. Now, employees knew exactly what was required of them as minimum standards for employment, in order to get the next raise, or to qualify for a promotion. After a detailed study, a sweeping revision of the hospital's wage and salary program became effective in October 1979, providing formalized and more equitable job classifications and pay schedules.

A Disciplinary/Grievance Procedure was established. An employee education program and a Supervisor's Training Course were instituted. Even Stress Management courses were offered.

Perhaps most indicative of the new president's management style was a weekly program called "Coffee with the President." Employees from various departments and employment levels were selected at random to meet with Cashman in the hospital board room for informal coffee and conversation. At first, many employees were surprised that such a program existed and skeptical that it would result in true dialogue with the president. When they discovered that this was a real opportunity to express their ideas and concerns, they were usually converted to positive members of the new Le Bonheur team.

Again, the efforts paid off. The nursing turnover rate dropped from 78% in 1977 to 18% in 1982, significantly lower than the 27% national average. The hospital-wide turnover rate fell to 36% in 1981 to 28% in 1982.

As soon as Cashman arrived at Le Bonheur, he made a personal trip to Chicago to meet with accreditation officials at JCAHO to request more time to correct the 125 deficiencies uncovered in the hospital's last evaluation. Just one year later, before 1978 was over, virtually all 125 deficiencies had been corrected, and Le Bonheur had received a two-year accreditation. Accreditation was renewed in 1980, and in 1982 it was extended to a three-year accreditation, the longest available.

Emboldened by Le Bonheur's direction and energy under its new president, the board of directors in July 1979 approved the biggest budget in the hospital's 27-year history. The new budget of nearly $21 million more than doubled the $9 million budget of just two years before. "I think the board had a lot of confidence after a short while that he was a good manager," says Dr. John Griffith, "so that allowed us to go forward in a way that was clearly accelerated because of his arrival."

Still, the biggest news of 1979 concerned the fulfillment of a vision that had been foreseen as far back as the hospital's opening.

To make sure that everything was being taken care of, Gene Cashman created a hotline that allowed parents in any patient room to dial his office directly.

More Seventies Smiles

Storekeeper Aubrey Trout.

Martha Hicks of Community Relations in 1979.

Robert K. Jones, Director of Community Relations and Development.

Fannie Ferguson, R.N. at her retirement party in 1977 after 23 years of service.

1976 Le Bonheur Club president Flo Hinson shows off the Club's Distinguished Community Service Award from the Tennessee Hospital Association.

Le Bonheur Club president Billie Ann Williams displays a proclamation from Governor Ray Blanton declaring it to be "Le Bonheur Week" in 1977.

Physical therapist Kathy Parker in 1979.

Admissions Administrator Brenita Crawford, seen here in 1978, was Le Bonheur's first Administrative Resident.

Bill Barbee of Biomedical Engineering.

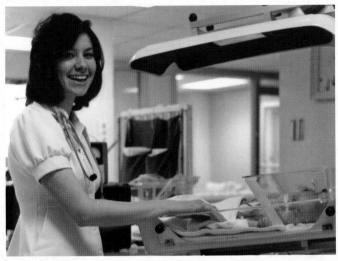

Glenda Brandon, R.N. watches a patient in the new Infant Care Unit in 1976.

Top nurse managers (left to right) Trenna Russell, Suzanne McCutheon, and Margaret Fizer.

Arthur Best served on Le Bonheur's board of directors from 1977 to 1992.

1978 Le Bonheur board member Dr. Joseph W. Westbrook.

Elmore Holmes III served on Le Bonheur's board of directors from 1973 to 1978.

Le Bonheur Club member Sharon Coleman models a t-shirt featuring the hospital's new mascot, "Scooter." The shirts were sold as a fundraiser for the hospital.

Vicki Stuart, R.N. and Laboratory Director Melvin Yow.

Respiratory therapist Andy Cox helps with the 1978 paper drive.

Le Bonheur Doctors in the Seventies

Dr. Gene Whitington, pediatric gastroenterology, joined the medical staff in 1956. He served on the hospital's board of directors in 1976 and was elected Chief of Staff in 1977.

1972 Chief of Staff Joseph Rothschild, M.D. shares a laugh with a young patient.

Dr. William Threlkeld, general pediatrics, joined the medical staff in 1962.

Dr. Shane Roy appears on the Marge Thrasher show.

Dr. Fred Barrett, pediatric infectious disease, arrived at Le Bonheur in 1978.

Le Bonheur/UT Pediatric Residency Program 1977 - 1978

First Row (left to right): Ralph Franeschini, Cecia Satterwhite, Rica Arnon, Riad Mardoum, John Griffith, Ethel Harrell, Robert Summitt, Aglae Koumbourli, Loraine Evans, Janice Algae, Helen Morrow. Second Row: Don Coughran, Emily Hamilton, Ellen Kang, James Etteldorf, Jim Brasfield, Joseph Fisher, Billy Arant, Larry Chien, Lou Parny. Third Row: Bill Wheeler, Ron Cordell, Jim Krindler, José Marin, David James, Courtney Anthony, Sid Wilroy, Thad Woodard, Jack Powell, Doug Bartley. Fourth Row: Joel Kronenberg, Michael Blaiss, John Williams, Marvin Gottlieb, George Burghen, Al Jones, Phillip George, Don Taylor, Richard Cowan, Bill Banner, Jr., Bob Tipton.

Dr. Peter F. Whitington, general pediatrics, in 1973.

David H. James, M.D. served on the 1973-74 Executive Committee of the Medical Staff.

Private pediatrician R. B. Miller, M.D. served on the hospital's board of directors and as president of the medical staff in 1973-74.

Dr. Webster Riggs, pediatric radiology, served on the 1973-74 Executive Committee of the Medical Staff.

Dr. Arika Arnon in 1976.

In 1977, Dr. James S. Brown headed the committee that coordinated the absorption of emergency cases formerly seen at Tobey Hospital.

Jimmy Brasfield, M.D. was Chief Resident at Le Bonheur in 1978.

Dr. John Hunter, seen here in 1978, worked in the Center for Children in Crisis, which serves abused and neglected children.

The Realization of a Dream Delayed

At the hospital's original dedication ceremony back in 1952 — when the ladies' heels were sinking into the asphalt and the keys to the hospital doors were floated away on balloons — U.T. Vice-President Dr. O. W. Hyman had correctly predicted the development of a comprehensive medical center in Memphis, and he had envisioned Le Bonheur as an integral part of it. Little did he know that Le Bonheur would surpass his vision to become a medical center in and of itself, a complete medical center just for children.

Le Bonheur's 1977 expansion would increase the size of the hospital by 85% and turn it into a true children's medical center. A new 106-room, four-story patient wing would replace the original 67-room wing built in 1952, which would henceforth be used to house administrative offices and ancillary services. The $13 million construction project would increase the hospital's bed capacity from 140 to 225.

The new facility would include outpatient therapy rooms that could accommodate 90,000 outpatients annually, about half of which would come from the Gailor Clinic at the City of Memphis Hospital. The old European-style medical amphitheater was to be replaced by a modern, 264-seat auditorium. Also included would be expanded research facilities, space for the Mid-South Poison Center, and a new Center for Children in Crisis.

Architect J. Wise Smith looked for ways to make the child-oriented nature of Le Bonheur inherent within its structure. In his original plan, a sixty-foot "castle-like" tower, clearly inspired by Disneyland's Cinderella Castle, rose above the hospital, helping to relieve the anxiety children might feel as they arrived. The tower was to include an elevator that patients and their parents could ride up for a view of the city.

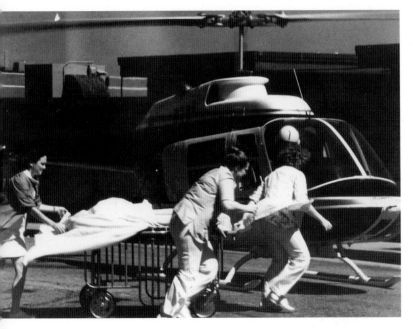

"This is about the time Disney was really getting on down in Orlando," says Smith. "So, we kind of conceived a castle, like the Magic Kingdom has, on top of the elevator tower. We thought it would be fun if the kids' first point into the hospital was to be the gateway. They'd go up into the castle and that's where their registration and acceptance into the hospital would be."

Other kid-enchanting ideas envisioned by Smith included a Japanese garden and even a petting zoo. Rising construction costs and less than unanimous approval from the board of directors caused these ideas to be deleted from the final plans, but extensive play areas and small garden niches would all be part of the new facility. Unfortunately, the large fountain that had been added to the new main entrance just three years before would have to be removed to make room for the growing hospital.

Mr. W. Neely Mallory was the general chairman of the fundraising campaign, which raised a total of $14.6 million. The Le Bonheur Club donated $208,500.00.

Metamorphosis

The 1977 expansion, combined with Le Bonheur's first addition just three years before, reshaped the hospital into a true children's medical center, giving it a new modern look in the process. Bed capacity would be nearly triple that of the original facility, and 28 outpatient clinics would accommodate up to 90,000 patients per year. The expansion would serve Le Bonheur's needs into the 1990s.

The hospital's main entrance was moved back onto Adams Avenue, but in a new location, and separate entrances remained on the east side of the hospital (right) for the outpatient clinics and emergency room. The original round medical amphitheater (still visible in the model above) was demolished and replaced with a modern auditorium.

This architectural rendering (looking north across Adams Avenue) emphasizes the new four-story, 106-room patient tower built on top of the three-story east wing that had been added just three years before.

Taking part in the groundbreaking on April 21, 1977 are (left to right) Dick Trippeer, board chairman, Dr. John Griffith, medical director and chairman of the UT Department of Pediatrics, Dr. Gene Whitington, chief of the medical staff, Fred Nowak, senior vice-president, and Billie Ann Williams, Le Bonheur Club president.

Right: The 1977 expansion begins with the addition of four floors of patient rooms to the top of the new east wing.

Above: The new main building adjacent to the patient tower would house everything from admissions and billing to ambulatory care and emergency services.

Right: As construction nears completion, the covering for Le Bonheur's new main entrance can be seen on the right.

Top: Former Le Bonheur Club president Beatrice Gerber, who played such a vital role in the construction of the original hospital, proudly shows off the expansion to a young patient, Billy Joe Hancock of Blue Mountain, Mississippi.

Left: "The Pit" is gone, and a new modern auditorium stands in its place.

Below left: Gene Cashman (third from left) who took over the reins of Le Bonheur in the middle of the construction project, inspects the progress. With him are (left to right) contractor David Martin, Director of Engineering Doug Platt, and architect Wise Smith

Below: Framed by the new construction, Scooter's career as Le Bonheur mascot draws to a close.

Above & right: The completed facility included an open-air Diorama.

The sleek lines and contemporary signage of the new facility showed that Le Bonheur was now a modern medical center.

The main entrance to the hospital was moved back to Adams Avenue, but in a new location. Visitors found the Admissions desk located conveniently inside the front door.

On the bottom floor of the hospital, a large subspecialty clinic area represented the new trend toward outpatient care.

A new 264-seat auditorium replaced the old European-style medical amphitheater.

Just as the hospital had when it first opened in 1952, the expanded medical center boasted the latest in health-care technology, whether it was in the laboratory (left) or the ICU (bottom).

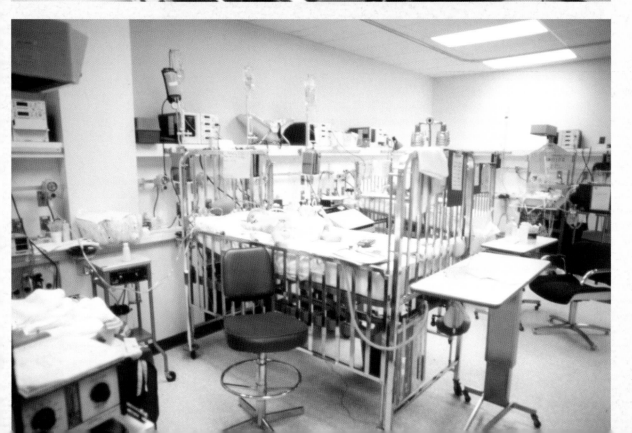

The new nursing stations provided nurses with greater visibility of the entire floor, while creating an atmosphere of openness for patients and their parents.

A quiet nook was found just off the main entrance on the south side of the building.

The West Patio remained a calm hideaway for visitors and staff.

A Nice Idea

In an effort to make Le Bonheur more kid-friendly, architect J. Wise Smith proposed a Disney-type castle at the top of an observation tower. While the idea didn't make it into the final plans, the new facility did include extensive play areas and small garden niches, as seen on the previous pages.

Castle 'Trademark' Is Included In Plans Of Le Bonheur's Medical Complex

Pediatric Complex Plan Nears Reality

By SCOTT WARE

Receiving the go-ahead yesterday for a $2-million community fund drive, officials at Le Bonheur Children's Hospital are completing plans to consolidate area pediatric services into a regional children's medical center.

The project will require an estimated $14.6 million in new construction to expand Le Bonheur's present facilities and to give the hospital a capacity for treating the combined public-private patient load planned for the center.

County government has already agreed to transfer its pediatric services to Le Bonheur from the Tobey unit of City of Memphis Hospital. In addition, the University of Tennessee Center for the Health Sciences will relocate its pediatric department at the facility.

After eight years of planning and development, hospital president Charles W. Bradley said the Le Bonheur center will ~ent a "prototype" for the develop- ~hildren's med: ~ters across

banker who is handling the financial arrangements.

He said the the hospital will depend on sales of tax-exempt revenue bonds this winter to provide most of the remaining $10 million for the project.

Contractors' bids are scheduled to be accepted in October, and if the financial arrangements are successful, officials say construction should begin by early next year. Completion time is projected at two years.

The new construction, which will increase the hospital's space by 85 per cent, will include a five-story addition atop the existing three patient floors completed in 1974. The addition will house 225 beds, an increase of 85 over the present bed capacity. The existing patient floors will be converted into office space for the UTCHS pediatric department.

Le Bonheur's outpatient facilities will be extensively remodeled and enlarged to accommodate an expected 90,000 annual visits from children in the 80-county area Le Bonheur serves. The figure includes the transfer of ~ ~patio ~is an'

trademark of what Bradley describes as an "un-hospital" atmosphere planned for the medical center. "The idea is that we're trying to make this an un-hospital. We're trying to relieve the anxiety of a child going into the hospital."

The castle, however, is dependent on the success of the hospital's financial plans, Bradley said. "There's one thing that's going to dictate whether we build the castle or not and that's cost. This will be a board decision. Whether or not the overall project is cut (after bids are received) will be the determining factor."

To further the "unhospital" atmosphere, plans also call for extensive children's play areas, a Japanese garden, a scenic diorama for plays and exhibits, a petting zoo and other recreational areas to be spread throughout the center.

The 225 patient beds will include 133 in private rooms equipped with baths and pull-down beds to accommodate parents wanting to stay with their children. For younger children whose parents are unable to ~ ~ ~center will ~th

Le Bonheur Children's Medical Center

Le Bonheur's new heart-shaped logo, designed in 1979 by local artist Bill Womack, is still in use today.

Additional funds of over $10 million came from the sale of tax-exempt revenue bonds. Equipping the new center would take an additional $2 million, and a separate Capital Fund Drive was launched for that purpose, with W. Neely Mallory again serving as chairman. Begun in 1976, this second drive ended less than a year later oversubscribed. The Le Bonheur Club contributed an additional $170,000 to that fund.

Groundbreaking for the new medical center took place on April 21, 1977. The most exciting moment of the two-year construction project came when all of Le Bonheur's patients were moved into the new patient tower, a delicate and complex mission. "We called it 'Operation Scooter,'" says then-Senior Vice President Fred Nowak, who supervised the move. "We got everybody involved and had a plan of greatest detail so that when the children were moved, floor by floor, from the old building into the new building, they didn't miss a medication, they didn't miss a meal, we didn't misplace any patients. There was no harm done. In fact, we made a big game of the whole thing and we all had a good time doing it."

"We all made cookies and brought cookies in," remembers Sallie Foster. "I was a 'runner.' Whenever they needed something, I put on my tennis shoes and off I went. It was a lot of fun. Actually it was a lot of work, but with everybody working together we had a lot of fun doing it."

The new Ambulatory Care Center opened its doors in October 1978 with twenty-eight subspecialty clinics. On November 2, 1978, the new 264-seat auditorium was used for the first time. In February 1979, the new patient wing was opened. Land was purchased for a third parking lot, and bright new signage featuring the hospital's new heart-shaped logo was installed. The landscaping around the new facility won an award from the City Beautiful Commission.

In October 1979, in recognition of the broad scope of services the hospital was now providing to the region, the board of directors voted to change the name of the hospital to Le Bonheur Children's Medical Center. The block of Adams Street east of Dunlap — over which the keys to the hospital door had floated away on that hot day so long ago — was changed by city proclamation to Children's Plaza, and the medical center's official street address became One Children's Plaza.

CHAPTER FOUR

Branching Out

I n 1980, the United States was still in the grips of a recession that had included skyrocketing inflation and gasoline shortages. American diplomats were being held hostage in Iran, and President Jimmy Carter, like Gerald Ford before him, was denied reelection. In Tennessee, Governor Ray Blanton faced extortion and conspiracy charges that would eventually land him in federal prison for 22 months.

Downtown Memphis was deserted — the major department stores had moved east, the flagship Peabody Hotel had declared bankruptcy, and even the Memphis Chamber of Commerce had gone out of business! The National Cotton Council moved the Maid of Cotton Pageant to Dallas, ending what had been a pivotal public event since 1931. The 1980 census showed the city's population at nearly 650,000, but that was a gain of only 40,000 from ten years before. The city's morale — like that of the country as a whole — was at an all-time low.

Suddenly, in January 1981, everything seemed to change. Within twenty-four hours of President Ronald Reagan's inauguration, the Iran hostages were freed. Reagan seemed capable of communicating his vision to the American people in a way unmatched by any president since John F. Kennedy. He and his wife Nancy's unapologetic glamour was embraced by Americans as a welcome change from twenty years of blue jeans and disco clothes, and before long, "yuppies" wearing "power ties" ushered in a renewed focus on career success (some said materialism) in America.

In the early 1980s, Federal Express led the rejuvenation of the Memphis economy. The reopening of The Peabody hotel, the renovation of Beale Street, and a new month-long celebration called Memphis in May began bringing people back downtown for social activities. By the mid-'80s, Memphis was in the middle of a growth spurt, with suburbs extending beyond the city limits into Hickory Hill, Germantown, and a sleepy rural whistle stop called Cordova.

Facing page and above: A little girl and her teddy bear receive the same treatment in Le Bonheur's first paid advertising campaign.

When Le Bonheur celebrated its thirtieth birthday in 1982, it had treated more than half a million children. In 1983, the hospital had 350 physicians on its medical staff, 866 employees, and an annual budget of $35 million. It was recognized as the pediatric referral center for the entire Mid-South, with a full 40% of its patients coming from outside the hospital's three-county primary service area. Le Bonheur was admitting more than 10,000 patients annually, as well as providing outpatient treatment to some 30,000 children through its 28 subspecialty clinics.

A Changing World

While Le Bonheur Children's Medical Center was clearly back on track, it was becoming increasingly obvious that it was also part of a regional and national healthcare system that was being impacted by a variety of new and complex factors. Technological advances and increasing specialization were saving more lives than ever, but they were also dramatically increasing the cost of healthcare. In the early '80s, healthcare spiraled up to 10% of the gross national product, generating a variety of responses that would help shape the industry to the present day. State and federal governments sought to rein in healthcare costs by reducing reimbursement through Medicaid and Medicare. Managed care mechanisms such as Health Maintenance Organizations (HMOs) and Preferred Provider Organizations (PPOs) appeared. Alternative delivery methods such as outpatient surgery and home healthcare were encouraged. At the same time, the standards for accrediting, licensing, and certifying healthcare organizations were being strengthened.

Margie Whitney, long-time night-shift nursing director, shares a smile with a patient.

Perhaps most importantly, competition was coming to healthcare. It began when some enterprising physicians opened the first "minor emergency clinics" in the late 1970s. In stark contrast to the traditional hospital emergency room, these clinics were fast, inexpensive, personal, and conveniently located. They quickly stole so much business from area emergency rooms that they prompted the first hospital advertising in Memphis.

The minor emergency clinics forced hospitals to ask themselves a simple question: "Are we doing the best job we can of delivering healthcare in the manner that is best suited to the patient's needs?" The answer, in many cases, was "No." Expanded outpatient services, same-day surgery, home healthcare, more personal attention, faster service, and conveniently located satellite facilities were just some of the ways that Memphis hospitals could better serve what were now being referred to for the first time as "customers."

"At that time, in healthcare, competition really was something new," says Donna Abney, Le Bonheur's first vice-

Remembering Bobby Allen

On September 15, 1981, Dr. Robert G. Allen, a Le Bonheur heart surgeon since the 1950s, was killed in an automobile accident. Admired for his skill and loved for his sense of humor, Dr. Allen's untimely death was a loss for the entire Le Bonheur family.

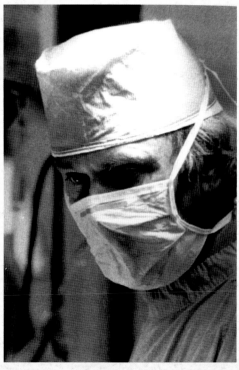
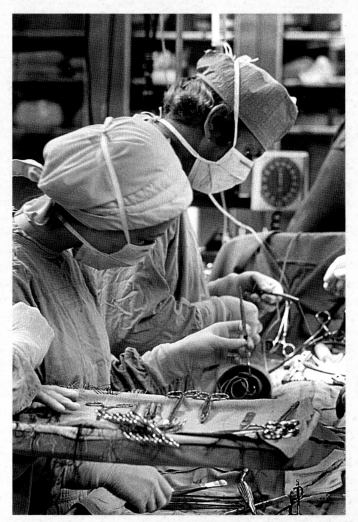
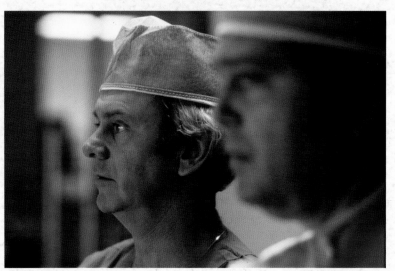

president of marketing. "We had to spend a lot of time helping the hospital staff and physicians understand that marketing was really just about pleasing the customer and being in touch with your customer and designing your products to meet the customer's needs."

In truth, Le Bonheur was already feeling the impact of competition. Its primary target market — young couples with children — had increasingly been moving out into the suburbs, where they were being served by a variety of new suburban hospitals. Methodist Hospital South had opened in Whitehaven in January 1973, and Doctors Hospital had opened on South Getwell later that same year. In 1974, St. Joseph East (now St. Francis) had opened its twenty-story tower on Park Avenue. The nine-story, 400-bed Baptist East Hospital had opened at Walnut Grove and I-240 in 1978, the same year Methodist North had opened on Austin Peay Highway in Raleigh.

In 1981, the consulting firm of M. Bostin & Associates submitted its final version of a formal long-range strategic plan commissioned by the hospital. The report not only emphasized the need to adapt to the complex new world of healthcare, it went so far as to question whether Le Bonheur could continue to survive as an independent, free-standing pediatric institution. If Le Bonheur were to make it to the end of the century, significant changes would have to be made.

To deal with this changing environment, President Gene Cashman pulled together a young and energetic management team. Former vice-president Fred Nowak was elevated to Senior Vice-President, where he continued to serve as a stabilizing influence on the hospital until his retirement in 1985. The rest of the top management team were recruited from other healthcare institutions — and even

Research into the causes and cures of childhood diseases has always been an important part of Le Bonheur's mission.

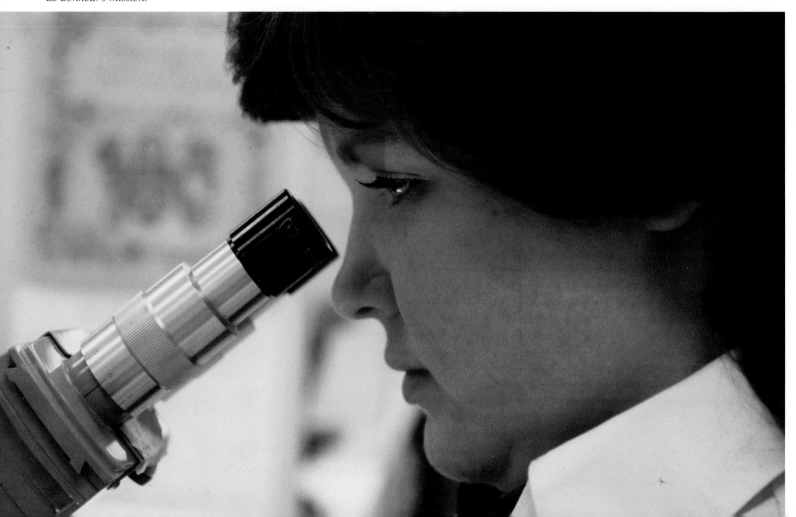

from other industries. Cashman wanted people who were energetic, dedicated, and young enough that they had not gotten used to running hospitals the same old way. "The one thing I knew about them before they came was that they were hard workers," he says. "I was willing to trade off any lack of experience or academic preparation for commitment and hard work."

"Mr. Cashman put together just a phenomenal management team," says Sallie Foster. "Sharp, bright, really interested, really concerned, really wanting the hospital to grow and to be the best, and I firmly believe that all of that effort together made it the best."

"The team got along extremely well," says David Stevens, who served as vice-president of Professional Services. "It was an open forum. We could disagree as much as we wanted with Gene. He wanted different views. We didn't always agree, and that was okay as long as we were in the room discussing these issues. But once we left that room, we all supported whatever decision had been made and went forward."

"Gene was not afraid to be challenged," says Donna Abney. "He did not always have to be right. Behind closed doors, we fought and yelled and screamed at each other, but that is what, ultimately, caused us to make good decisions instead of bad ones."

"They were smart, talented people," says Cashman of his team, "and they worked together to build a great system. And they've all remained very good friends."

The new management team at work. Left to right: David Stevens, VP of Professional Services, Jennifer Jenkins, VP of Nursing Services, Gene Cashman, President, and Larry Bryan, Chief Financial Officer.

Pediatric heart surgeon Dr. Tom Watson and cardiologist Dr. Tom Discenza formed the core of Le Bonheur's new heart program, established in the 1980s.

Le Bonheur's New Management Team

During his first several years as Le Bonheur's president and CEO, Gene Cashman pulled together a young and energetic management team. Over the next ten years, this team would fundamentally reshape Le Bonheur and its approach to delivering healthcare services.

Eugene K. Cashman
President

Born in 1941, Eugene K. Cashman, Jr. was the son of a construction contractor and a hospital dietitian. A native of Savannah, Georgia, he received his bachelors degree in business and finance at Auburn University. Direct commissioned into the Army Medical Service Corps during the Vietnam conflict, he spent three and a half years in the Army Surgeon General's Office in Washington. He then entered the American University to obtain his Masters of Science in computer science and management information systems, and while there he took an administrative position at Children's Hospital National Medical Center. He set up the hospital's first computer system and eventually supervised the construction of its new facility. He was recruited to run Le Bonheur in November 1977. He remained president of the hospital

until 1995. With the merger of Le Bonheur Children's Medical Center and Methodist Health Systems, the parent company was reorganized as a philanthropic organization that distributes grants to fund programs and services aimed at improving the well-being of children. "Gene Cashman is a visionary," says Donna Abney, "irreverent, fun, verbal, a wonderful person to work for. He is a risk taker. He is also a funny, funny man. I remember the Halloween he walked all over the hospital with a Richard Nixon mask on. I remember his stereo being played so loudly in his office that the walls of my office were shaking. Imagine having to call your own boss and asking him to turn his music down."

Fred Nowak
Senior Vice President

Frederick F. Nowak was working with the mentally ill at Arlington Developmental Center when he was hired in 1974 by Le Bonheur president Bill Bradley to serve as Chief Operating Officer. Well-liked for his friendly and even-handed approach to matters, he helped guide the hospital through the major construction projects of the late seventies. He served as acting president during the search that brought Gene Cashman to the hospital. When the management structure was revised, his title

changed to Senior Vice President. When he retired in May 1985, the hospital presented him with a fishing boat in lieu of the traditional gold watch. "I'm still fishing with that boat," he says today, "trout fishing. I've got a trailer up on the Little Red River and I've got the boat in the water, so I go there once a month for three or four days and fish."

Donna Abney
Vice President of Marketing

Donna Abney, a native of New Orleans, received her degree in journalism from the University of Memphis in 1974. She was the marketing director at a manufacturing firm when she met Jennifer Jenkins in the university's Executive MBA program. She was hired as Director of Marketing in January 1983 at the age of 29, and promoted to Vice President of Marketing a year later. Maintaining a delicate balance in an industry in which marketing and advertising were still dirty words, she convinced physicians and administrators alike that Le Bonheur could better serve the children of the Mid-South by expanding its programs and becoming more customer friendly. "Donna really brought a new thought process to us," says David Stevens. "While we thought we were being service-oriented, she made sure that we were more consumer-oriented." Soon after her arrival, Donna tackled the immense new issue of managed care, negotiating contracts with every major provider in the region. Today, she serves as Senior Vice President of Methodist Health Systems and is a member of the Le Bonheur Foundation board of directors.

David Stevens
Vice President of Professional Services

David Stevens grew up in Pulaski, Tennessee and earned his undergraduate degree in accounting and finance at the University of Tennessee at Knoxville. While completing his MBA at the University of Memphis, he served as an administrator for Doctors Hospital in Memphis and for a large medical group. In 1979, at the age of 26, he was hired by Le Bonheur as Assistant Vice President for Ambulatory Care, but was elevated to vice president in less than a year. The quintessential "Type A" personality, David helped restructure Le Bonheur's ambulatory care department and worked to improve the hospital's relation with referring and staff physicians. Then, as chief operating officer of Southern Health Systems, he built a successful network of subsidiary businesses that eventually generated $135 million in yearly revenues. Today he is chairman and CEO of Accredo, one of the

companies he helped build. "David's personality is a 'take no prisoners' kind of personality," says Donna Abney. "We would design a new program and he would be halfway out the door implementing it before the ink had dried on the paper."

Jennifer Jenkins
Vice President of Nursing Services

Jennifer Jenkins was hired as Le Bonheur's first Vice President of Nursing in 1978 at the age of 30. She had previously served as Director of Nursing at East Tennessee Children's Hospital in Knoxville. Jennifer remained at Le Bonheur until 1987, when she left to do consulting work. She now lives in Denver, Colorado and works for LifeMasters Supported SelfCare.

Larry Bryan
Chief Financial Officer

A native of Winona, Mississippi, Larry Bryan received his accounting degree from the University of Mississippi in 1975. He was hired as Director of the Accounting Department at Hines

Hospital in Jackson, then promoted to Chief Financial Officer. In 1980, at the age of 28, he came to Le Bonheur as CFO. "My first week on the job," he says, "Gene sent me a copy of the engagement letter he had with the search firm that brought me here. I had managed to negotiate the very bottom nickel of the salary range they had been willing to pay." Although Southern Health Systems hired its own CFO early on, Larry still played a vital role in setting up each subsidiary and negotiating contracts. Larry left Le Bonheur in November 1993 to start Diversified Trust Company in Memphis, where he remains today.

Garry Maness
Vice President of Administrative & Support Services

Garry Maness was working in the Human Resources department of Baptist Memorial Hospital when he was recruited in 1979 at the age of 32 to serve as Le Bonheur's Director of Personnel. The next year he was promoted to Vice-President, Administrative & Support Services. In 1989 he became Vice-President, Facilities Planning & Construction for Le Bonheur Health Systems, Inc. He served as Senior Vice-President of Development for the hospital from 1993 until his departure in 1996. Today he is a commercial real estate agent with Crye-Leike.

Branching Out

In the early '80s, the new management team continued to lead Le Bonheur through a series of internal improvements. New equipment was purchased for laser surgery, CT scans, and a cardiac cath lab. A Parents Resource Center was established, which published a much-utilized Parents Handbook. Pediatric seminars were held for community emergency room personnel. Quality Assurance and Guest Relations programs were begun. Infant Stimulation activities were adopted by Nursing Services. A free telephone Physician Referral Service was started. An annual "Day of Sharing" was begun at local churches for those who had lost a child or sibling, giving them an opportunity to receive support from others who had experienced the same loss.

A Physicians Relations program was initiated to ensure that the needs of the referring physicians were being met. For the first time in the hospital's history,

Dr. Greg Stidham, director of the Intensive Care Unit (center of photo), provides training to his staff in the recently expanded facility.

representatives went out and visited with Le Bonheur's most important gatekeepers, not just in Memphis, but in surrounding counties throughout west Tennessee, north Mississippi, and east Arkansas. What they found surprised them. "We saw ourselves as the mecca and the center of pediatric healthcare," says Donna Abney. "We just assumed that referring physicians had to be grateful for what we provided. But we found that there was a lot of dissatisfaction with Le Bonheur, not with the clinical side, but with the operational side, the communications side, the responsiveness side. Often, if a physician had an option on where to refer, they were going elsewhere, because Le Bonheur was not a physician-friendly user environment. We set out to change that."

Most importantly, the Cashman team began to look at the institution in relation to the local, regional, and national healthcare markets. They carefully studied children's hospitals across the country, searching for new ways to better serve the pediatric population of the Mid-South. Their analysis suggested that Le Bonheur needed to expand its vision. "We knew that healthcare for pediatrics wasn't just inside the four walls of the hospital," says David Stevens. "For Le Bonheur, our healthcare mission was to provide care regardless of where the patient was and what services they needed."

In February 1983, the management team recommended, and the board of directors authorized, a corporate restructure that would position Le Bonheur to achieve an expanded vision while also protecting the hospital's long-term financial independence. A new parent corporation was formed, originally named Southern Child Care but later changed to Le Bonheur Health Systems, Inc. This not-for-profit umbrella organization would own Le Bonheur Children's Medical Center, as well as other subsidiary organizations or agencies both for-profit and not-for-profit. Le Bonheur Health Systems, Inc. used this avenue to take Le Bonheur's expertise outside the hospital walls.

The for-profit arm was designated as Southern Health Systems, and before long it was operating a variety of companies:

Infusion therapies at PharmaThera are mixed in state-of-the-art "clean rooms" by pharmacists experienced in providing specialized medications.

- A home health agency providing home nursing, respiratory therapy, physical therapy, and speech therapy for pediatric and adult patients.
- A home infusion therapy service originally named Southern Health Resources, but changed in 1988 to PharmaThera. A licensed pharmacy with mixing stations in Memphis, Nashville, Birmingham, and Jackson (Mississippi), PharmaThera provided clinical support and technology in the home for pediatric and adult patients. Therapies included home antibiotic treatment, home hyperalimentation, home chemotherapy, and home enteral services. The company also contracted to provide inpatient infusion therapy services in acute care hospitals.

Patient education plays an important role in calming the fears of children receiving healthcare, whether in the hospital or in the home. Teaching dolls and specialized equipment help meet the needs of PharmaThera's pediatric patients.

- A temporary nurse staffing agency originally called Professional Health Care (later changed to CliniCall), which provided temporary nurses, physical therapists, respiratory therapists, and medical technologists for staffing at hospitals, in nursing homes, and for individuals seeking private duty care.
- A durable medical equipment company originally known as MedCare (later changed to HealthEffects).
- NovaFactor, a national distributor of biotech pharmaceuticals.

By the mid-1990s, the various subsidiaries of Southern Health Systems had ten offices in eight states, with NovaFactor delivering pharmaceuticals to patients throughout the nation. PharmaThera had grown to be one of the ten largest infusion therapy providers in the nation. Ultimately, fewer than 5% of SHS patients came from Le Bonheur. In 1995, Southern Health Systems generated an astounding $135 million in revenue.

"Le Bonheur was one of the earliest home care providers in the country," says David Stevens, who served as chief operating officer of Southern Health Systems. "There had been a couple of others, but we were one of the earliest. The parameters were that we wanted to be able to take care of any child being discharged out of Le Bonheur, no matter what their needs were."

According to pediatrician Dr. Phillip George, it worked. "The availability of high tech pediatric home care — and to me, Southern Health Systems' pediatric home care was as good as any in the nation — was a great advantage to the child and the family. First of all, no children want to come to the hospital; they would rather be at home and so would the family. From the standpoint of the psychosocial aspects of taking care of children, there is little doubt that it was a great advance."

"This was a real win-win situation for everyone," says Gene Cashman. "Not only is it better for children to receive treatment in the comfort of their own homes, it's also cheaper for both the parent and the hospital. This new direction helped preserve Le Bonheur's limited resources for the very sick children who really needed to be in a hospital."

"The vision of creating a parent company and launching into other business lines was one that many healthcare systems were beginning to seed at that time," says Donna Abney. "It was very topical in the healthcare literature at the time

The Golden Girls, a song-and-dance troupe made up of Le Bonheur Club members, provided entertainment at fundraising events.

that diversification was going to be an important part of success for the next decade." Le Bonheur, however, was the first pediatric hospital in the nation to develop such a comprehensive system, and it did so more aggressively than most adult hospitals.

"In fact," says David Stevens, "we helped a number of other hospitals, especially Seattle and Los Angeles, where we had consulting relationships with them. Throughout the years, we had a number of other consulting jobs with children's hospitals, in which we helped them unbundle their inpatient care as we had done."

Le Bonheur board member John Collier admits he had trouble keeping up with the rapid changes. "I told Gene Cashman that I needed a card or something to tell me the different elements of the business, and so he finally printed one up for me so I could look at it whenever we talked about it. But I think the board was solidly behind Gene Cashman because he had taken us out of a fairly tough period."

"We ended up being profitable on a consistent basis through that time," says Larry Bryan, who served as Senior Vice President of Finance. "That allowed us to build our cash reserves to ever greater levels."

Going Outside the Hospital Walls

In the mid-'80s, a variety of subsidiaries were created in order to take Le Bonheur's expertise beyond the hospital walls. The following story, reprinted from the hospital's employee newsletter, demonstrates how these cutting-edge efforts helped Le Bonheur fulfill its mission to do "whatever it takes" for children.

Home Care Allows Bryan Norton To Live Normal Life of 8-Year-old Kid

(Reprinted from the *Le Bonheur News*, September 1988)

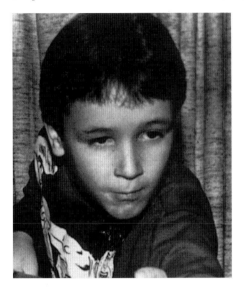

Eight-year-old Bryan Norton plays summer baseball, roughhouses with his brothers Charles, 9, and Junior, 15, and currently prefers the company of his six dogs over little girls. In most ways, he is a typical, healthy little boy. His good health is the result of early intervention by Le Bonheur Pediatric Gastroenterologist Gene L. Whitington, M.D., and the capabilities of Le Bonheur Health Systems, Inc.

For 10 hours each night, Bryan receives life-sustaining nutrients and liquids through an IV in a process called parenteral nutrition (PN). PharmaThera, Inc., a division of Le Bonheur Health Systems, Inc., provides Bryan with the supplies and equipment to receive his treatments at home.

"Parenteral nutrition, also called hyperalimentation, is necessary for patients whose gastrointestinal tracts don't function normally," Dr. Whitington explains. "Bryan is given a special IV which contains all the nutrients he needs for normal growth and development."

When Bryan was diagnosed two weeks after birth with intractable diarrhea, David and Linda Norton worried about a normal life for their son. With the help of home care, Bryan has adapted — even learning how to walk pushing an IV pole.

"Intractable diarrhea, a hereditary dysfunction which cannot be surgically corrected, depletes Bryan's body of much-needed nutrients and liquids," Dr. Whitington says. "Without daily PN, the result would be malnutrition, dehydration, and possibly death.

"We were very apprehensive when the doctors explained to us about catheters and IVs and the whole hyperalimentation process. Then we met a chubby, healthy baby at Le Bonheur who was on hyperalimentation and we saw its life-saving benefits for Bryan," Mrs. Norton remembers. After four months at Le Bonheur, they returned home to Middleton, Tennessee, with Bryan in their arms.

For two years, Bryan and his parents made weekly trips to Le Bonheur to pack an ice chest with a week's worth of PN supplies. The solutions were pre-mixed by hospital pharmacists and administered daily at home by Bryan's parents. When Bryan was nearly 2, his parents began mixing the solutions themselves at home.

In 1984, PharmaThera began supplying Bryan's hyperalimentation needs with convenient home delivery, Mrs. Norton said. Pleased with the service they received, last year the family turned over the task of mixing the PN solutions to pharmacists at PharmaThera.

"Having pharmacists mix the solutions has eased tremendous pressure off of me. Now I just go to the refrigerator and get a premixed bag," notes a relieved Mrs. Norton. PharmaThera also delivers special requests and picks up lab work when it is collected at home.

Each night at 9, Mrs. Norton cycles Bryan on the PN solution and increases the amount at 10 p.m. During the night, she gets up every two or three hours to check the catheter, line, pumps, and filters. "It's something you get used to after awhile," she says. Bryan cycles off PN each morning at 7, just in time for second grade classes at Middleton Elementary School.

"Bryan is probably healthier than a lot of kids his age. He doesn't let hyperalimentation get in his way. He plays as hard as most boys his age, but he knows to be careful with his catheter. We don't treat him any different," Mrs. Norton says.

"The benefits of home care are lower costs and freedom for the patient to be with his family," Dr. Whitington notes. "Most importantly for Bryan, that means a normal childhood."

Satellites & Partnerships

Le Bonheur's newfound financial stability allowed it to take steps to better serve the expanding suburbs of Memphis:

- In February 1985, Le Bonheur East opened just off Poplar at Estate. The facility provides subspecialty outpatient clinics during the day and an acute care clinic at night.
- In 1988, Le Bonheur Bartlett was opened on Stage Road. Containing 10,000 square feet of space, the facility houses pediatric subspecialist offices, a diagnostic area, a full-time otolaryngology practice, and the Le Bonheur/UT Memphis Day Treatment Program, an alternative program for children with emotional and behavioral problems.
- In January 1990, the Le Bonheur DeSoto Doctors Offices opened at 7502 Airways. Similar to Le Bonheur East and Le Bonheur Bartlett, the new facility includes a diagnostic center that allows children to have tests run prior to admission to the hospital.
- Later that same year, the Le Bonheur East Day Surgery Center, a one-day outpatient surgery facility, opened next to Le Bonheur East.

During this period, the hospital also entered into several partnerships that more closely connected it to the area's medical community:

- Hospital Wing, the first community-wide air ambulance service, equally owned and shared by four hospitals.
- The Memphis Center for Stone Disease, a lithotripsy center for the non-invasive removal of kidney stones, formed in 1986 as a joint medical service of several local hospitals.
- Med Express, a national overnight laboratory testing service using Federal Express as the delivery arm.

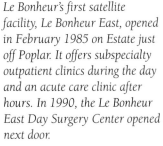

Le Bonheur's first satellite facility, Le Bonheur East, opened in February 1985 on Estate just off Poplar. It offers subspecialty outpatient clinics during the day and an acute care clinic after hours. In 1990, the Le Bonheur East Day Surgery Center opened next door.

Le Bonheur didn't limit its partnerships to the Memphis area. Child Health Corporation of America was formed as a joint venture between eighteen children's hospitals to explore business opportunities on a national scale and to achieve savings through group purchasing. Southern Pediatric Hospitals was a consortium of five southern hospitals that shared medical and management expertise. Le Bonheur also became more active than ever in the National Association of Children's Hospitals and Related Institutions (NACHRI).

At the same time, Le Bonheur sought new ways to partner with physicians throughout its referral area, including its own medical staff. Two professional corporations — Le Bonheur Pediatric Subspecialists, P.C. and Le Bonheur Pediatrics, P.C. — allowed pediatricians to better position themselves for contracting with managed care plans and other alternative delivery systems. By combining the services of Le Bonheur, its physician corporations, and Southern Health Systems, the hospital positioned itself to thrive in the new era of managed care. "It was a real powerful force for us in managed care," says David Stevens. "It allowed us to be a part of every managed care contract in the city, which no one else was."

Le Bonheur was one of four hospitals that shared ownership and management of the city's first community-wide air ambulance service, Hospital Wing.

"One of the things that I never saw at Le Bonheur was an unwillingness to look at any and everything," says Larry Bryan. "I think the easiest thing to do in a non-profit healthcare organization is just to say, 'Let's let everybody else do things and if it works, we'll go piggyback it.' That's not the way we operated."

Images of the Eighties:
Le Bonheur Physicians

By the 1980s, Le Bonheur had the widest selection of pediatric subspecialists in a three-state region.

Robert A. Price, M.D., Chief of Pathology and Director of Laboratory Services

Dr. Phil George addresses a group of medical students.

Pediatric surgeon Dr. Santiago Vera helped establish Le Bonheur's liver transplant program.

Dr. Stuart Birnbaum, pediatric cardiology.

Dr. Fred Rivera, pediatric hematology/oncology.

Dr. Charles Gross, pediatric otolaryngology, served as Chief of Staff 1987-88.

Dr. Robert Crumrine, pediatric anesthesiology.

Dr. Kip Frizzell, general pediatrics.

Dr. Dan Shell, plastic and reconstructive surgery.

Dr. David Bell, pediatric cardiology.

The 1983 UT/Le Bonheur Department of Pediatrics

First Row (left to right): John Ellis, Pat Wall, Jim Hughes, Glenn Silber, Jewell Ward, John Griffith, Willie Tsiu, June Joyner, Henrietta Bada, Abby Wasserman, James Etteldorf, Shane Roy, Henry Herrod, Phillip George. Second Row: Nancy Pattison, Elaine Pugh, Gene Whitington, Steven Smith, Avrachan Tharapel, David James. Third Row: Susan Orenstein, Pat Flynn, Dick Cook, Fred Rivara, George Burghen, Ellan Kang, Linda Pfifer, Marilyn Robinson. Fourth Row: Joan Kyle, Debbie Jones, Anita Hill Powell, Sandy Feldman, Cathy Stevens. Fifth Row: Dunk Eastham, Nestor Ramiez, Yana Banks, Rick Sheridan, Kip Frizzell, Cindy Moore, Jennifer Luellen, Bruce Jenkins, Peter Whitington, Fred Barrett, Gary Bell, Charles Fitch, Frank Gillotti, David Orenstein, Lloyd Crawford, Winfred Wang, Bob Greene, David Bell, Stevens Melton, Jerry Heston, Robert Wilroy, Allen Lenoir, Bubba Edwards, Wayne Furman.

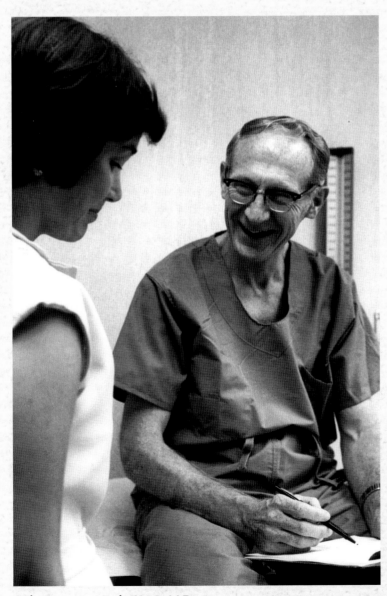

Pediatric surgeon Earle Wrenn, M.D. puts a parent at ease.

Dr. Emmett Bell, Jr. served as Chief of Staff 1986-87.

Dr. Bruder Stapleton, pediatric endocrinology.

Dr. Bruce Jenkins, pediatric neonatology, in 1988.

Dr. Gerald Presbury, general pediatrics, in 1988.

Dr. Loyd Crawford, pediatric allergies.

Dr. Sid Wilroy, pediatric genetics.

Dr. Gerald Jerkins, pediatric urology.

Dr. Bill May, pediatric neurology.

Dr. Joseph Weinberg came to Le Bonheur in 1985 as director of the Emergency Department.

Dr. Gerald Golden, pediatric neurology.

Dr. George Burghen, pediatric endocrinology.

Dr. Robert Sanford, pediatric neurosurgeon.

On June 17, 1987, former Le Bonheur Medical Director John Griffith, M.D. (second from right) was presented with a portrait of himself that still hangs in Le Bonheur. Present at the reception honoring Dr. Griffith were (left to right), Gene Cashman, Le Bonheur president, Donald Schuppe, former Le Bonheur board chairman, and current board chairman John Collier.

Pediatric surgeon Douglas Hixson, M.D., served as Chief of Staff 1989-90.

Dr. Bob Boehm, pediatric neurology.

Dr. Roger Hiatt, pediatric ophthalmology, fits a child for glasses.

Dr. Bruce Alpert, pediatric cardiology.

Dr. Norman Noe, pediatric urology.

Dr. Michael Bond, pediatric dermatology.

Dr. J. T. Jabbour, pediatric neurology.

Dr. Gene Whitington is interviewed by Channel 13 news anchor Pam Crittenden as part of the hospital's community education efforts.

Images of the Eighties:
Nursing Services

During the 1970s and 1980s, the field of nursing rose to a new level of professionalism and specialization. Under the leadership of Jennifer Jenkins, Vice President of Nursing Services, Le Bonheur helped pioneer such concepts as primary care nursing and decentralized management.

Robin Wade, R.N., Assistant Director of Nursing in the Special Care Unit, receives the 1986 Le Bonheur Nurse of the Year Award from Jennifer Jenkins, VP Nursing (right).

Outpatient Clinics nurse Virginia Manning, R.N., B.S.N.

Anne Sams, R.N., Director of Nursing, 7th Floor Surgical Unit in 1985.

Suzanne Howard, R.N., was appointed Director of Support Services in September 1984.

ECMO Coordinator Deborah Chyka, R.N., M.S.N., C.C.R.N.

Glenda Grandon, R.N., Recovery Room, was Le Bonheur's Employee of the Month for July 1984.

Lea Ann Byrd, R.N., was the 1987 Le Bonheur Nurse of the Year.

Clinical Nurse Specialist Linda Ware, R.N., M.S.N.

Lisa Payton, R.N., Nursing Administrator for the Southern Health Systems home health agency, a Le Bonheur subsidiary.

Pat Worley, R.N., M.S.N., was a Clinical Care Specialist in the Ambulatory Care Department.

Penny Stewart, R.N., B.S.N., ER Nurse Educator.

Nurse Manager Susan Daw, R.N., M.S.N., was Le Bonheur's 1989 Nurse of the Year.

Jamie Holmes, R.N., Clinical Nurse Specialist, Director of the Nurse Intern Program.

ER Director Betsy Cannon, R.N.

Physician Liaison Coordinator Pam Brewer, R.N.

Krista James, R.N., B.S.N., was named Ambulatory Care Nurse Supervisor in 1984.

Rod Corbitt, R.N.

Patients are welcomed to the Day Care Unit by (left to right) Cathy Philpot, unit secretary, Mani Young, L.P.N. II, and Jennilyn Jennings, R.N. Jennilyn was Le Bonheur's Employee of the Month for May 1986.

Marcella Lawrence, R.N., M.S.N., Clinical Nurse Specialist, Genetics.

Sharon Hopkins, R.N., Director of Nursing, Special Care Unit.

Jackie Harty, R.N.

Susan Helms, R.N., B.S.N., served as Director of the ICU & Progressive Care Unit before becoming Director of Injury Prevention.

Carla Dillard was a Nurse Recruiter in 1987. She later became an Assistant Director of Nursing.

The ICU staff named its Nurse of the Year award after April Lewis (below) following her tragic death in a car accident. To the right, Mary Pat Hartman, R.N. receives the first April Lewis Award in September 1985 from Jennifer Jenkins, VP Nursing and Greg Stidham, M.D., Director of Critical Care Services.

Michelle Fabery, R.N., Clinical Nurse Educator in the Emergency Department.

Nancy Miller, R.N., M.S.N., was named Pediatric Nurse Fellowship Coordinator in 1986.

Ralph Hawkins, R.N. in 1988.

Betsy Beazley, R.N., Assistant Director of Nursing, Emergency Department in 1985.

In May 1985, Glen Ann Martin, R.N., M.S.N., Mental Health Clinical Nurse Specialist, was a co-recipient of the first annual Le Bonheur Nurse of the Year Award, along with ICU Nurse Elesia Turner, R.N.

Elizabeth Wortham Brewster, Director of Education, in 1988.

OR Director Sandy Hubbert, R.N., B.S.N.

Images of the Eighties:

Le Bonheur Employees at Work & Play

Right: Cathy Weaver, Dietetics Director (center), enjoys a Le Bonheur employee picnic with staff members Lorreta Jameson (left) and Dorothy Houston.

Sallie Foster, Executive Secretary to Le Bonheur president Gene Cashman, is congratulated by Shelby County Mayor Bill Morris (left) after being named 1984 Secretary of the Year by the Memphis chapter of Professional Secretaries International.

Bill Hancock, R.R.T., Director of Respiratory Therapy and Pedi-Flight Coordinator, and Cynthia Broner, M.D., check equipment on the two new Bell 222UT helicopters made available to Le Bonheur in 1986 as a result of the Hospital Wing consortium. Hancock was Le Bonheur's Employee of the Month in January 1983.

Le Bonheur's Employee Advisory Committee helped enhance communication across all levels of the hospital. Members of the committee in 1984 were (front row, left to right) Ester Patrick, Unit Secretary, Seventh Floor; Karen Roberson, R.N., Surgery; Vivian Emery, Dietetics Clerk; Diane Fabick, Supervisor, Respiratory Therapy; and Becky Carpentar, Secretary, Nursing. Standing are Cindy Rector, Committee Chairman, Insurance Clerk; Diane Neal, Committee Co-Chairman, Administrative Supervisor, Emergency Department; Wayne Johnson, Shift Engineer; Sabrina Para, R.N., Recovery Room Nurse; Pat Bledsoe, Information Systems Supervisor; and Gloria Phillips, Accounts and Receivable Clerk.

EEG Technician Cissy Asbridge, November 1988 Employee of the Month.

Ed Coleman, Director of Public Relations.

Kathy Huggins, Patient Service Representative.

Janet Phillips joined Le Bonheur in July 1988 as Director of Marketing.

Jim New, Administrator, Department of Pediatrics.

Susan Owens, Purchasing, May 1983 Employee of the Month.

Bob Winkler, CPA, Operations Auditor.

Rich Helms, Pharm D., Director of Clinical Pharmacy.

Pat Raburn, Executive Secretary, February 1985 Employee of the Month.

Bernice Warren, Chief Cook, Employee of the Month for January 1987.

Sarah Cobb, Lab Supervisor, night shift.

John Shearer, Director of Security.

Housekeeping supervisor Josephuf Burnside in 1984.

Shirley Smith, the 1986 Employee of the Year.

Darryl Davis, Telecommunications.

Above: Ruth Ann Hale, PR Coordinator, and Janet Marks, Administration, display a proclamation from the Shelby County Mayor announcing "Le Bonheur Week."

Left: Elizabeth Ostric, Administrative Resident and later a VP.

Nick Ring, Accounting.

Raymond Ware, Biomedical Engineering, August 1983 Employee of the Month.

Louise Jackson, Dietary, November 1989 Employee of the Month.

Brenda Morris, Personnel, Employee of the Month for January 1985.

Physical therapist Sarah Burton Dormois.

Stephen Anderson joined Le Bonheur in 1988 as Director, General Services.

Marler Stone, Director of Development.

Risha Hoover, Admissions, November 1982 Employee of the Month.

Jaime Fernandez, Operations Manager in the Laboratory, in 1985.

Hazel Harlan, Development, Employee of the Month for December 1984.

Lela Bruce, Medical Records, June 1985 Employee of the Month.

Dowtin Martin, Director of Ambulatory Services.

Ben Taylor, Print Shop Director.

Ed Roberts, Director of Physical Therapy.

Vernie Mae Lemons, assistant laundry supervisor, Le Bonheur's Employee of the Year in 1985.

Arthur Johnson, Environmental Services technician, 1988 Employee of the Year.

Catherine Hobson, Rehabilitation Services aide, Employee of the Year in 1989.

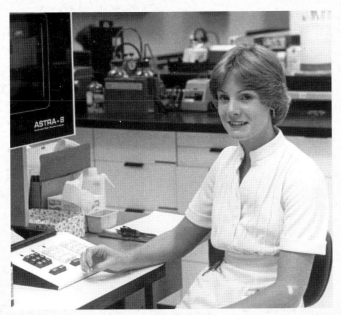

Debbie Mac Brewster, Laboratory.

Samuel Newson, Day Supervisor (left) and Sterling Robinson, Night Supervisor, plan shift schedules for the Environmental Services Department in 1986.

Members of the 1984 Le Bonheur Women's Softball team were (first row, left to right) Bobbie Hamilton, Karen Roberson, Sue Webster, and Sandy Williams. (Second row) Laura Smith, Debbie Steward, Kere Hall, Beverly Nix, and Tish Coghill. (Third row) Coach Don Hall, Jackie Griggs, Teresa Medlin, and Coach Keith Thornton.

Images of the Eighties:

Why We're Here

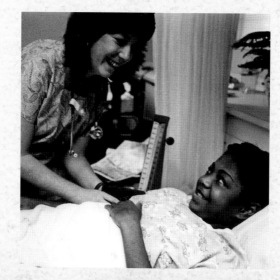

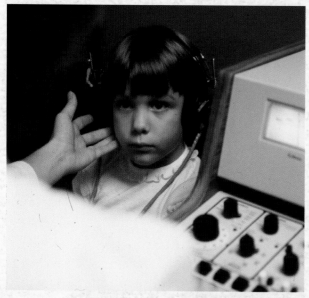

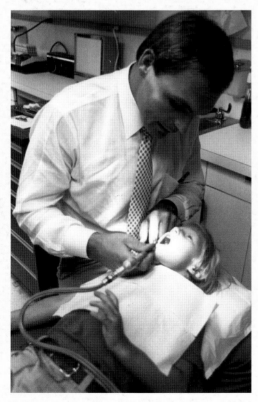

Larry Dormois, D.D.S., examines Andy Whitten, age 5, in the new Pediatric Dentistry Clinic in 1985.

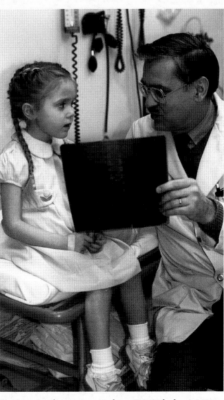

Private pediatrician Robert W. Riikola, M.D., explains a radiograph to Casey Pulliam at the Le Bonheur East Night Clinic in 1986.

Sandy Wasson, R.N., gets a hug from an appreciative patient.

Continuing the Tradition

Meanwhile, as always, Le Bonheur stayed on the cutting edge of medical technology. A pediatric liver transplant program was begun in 1983, at that time one of only four in the country. Starting in 1986, Le Bonheur offered microvascular tissue transfer, a surgical process that uses a patient's healthy tissue and arteries to reconstruct severely injured limbs. In June 1987, the first heart transplant was performed in the hospital's new Heart Center.

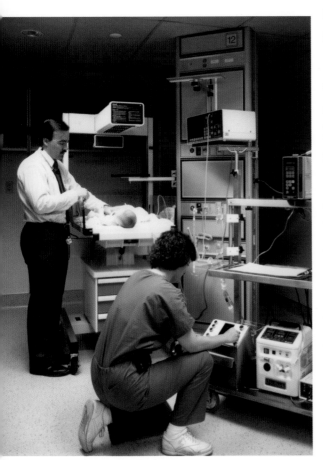

In 1988, Le Bonheur helped pioneer laser surgery, which allows doctors to remove blockages without invasive surgery. The hospital also started offering Extra Corporeal Membrane Oxygenation, or ECMO. This heart-lung bypass machine takes over the functions of the heart and lungs in infants for up to ten days, giving damaged lungs time to heal.

In 1989, the highly respected Campbell's Clinic began providing orthopedic services at the hospital. A Kidney Center and an Allergy/Immunology Center were opened, and Le Bonheur's Diabetes Center was one of only three pediatric facilities in the nation to gain recognition from the American Diabetes Association for meeting its high standards.

Le Bonheur continued to lead the way not only in medical services, but also in quality-of-life services. In recognition of the psychological needs of children, the PET Program (Preparation Encourages Trust) used puppet shows, coloring books, and other tools to prepare young children for their upcoming hospital stay. Kaleidoscope, Le Bonheur's cultural enrichment program, brought the visual, literary, and performing arts into the lives of patients, families, and staff. In 1988, the program won the Governor's Special Citation Award in the Arts.

Technicians demonstrate the new ECMO equipment, a heart-lung bypass machine that gives damaged lungs time to heal.

In 1982, the hospital dedicated its new "Tree of Life" donor recognition wall sculpture to the honor of founding member Elizabeth Gilliland, the lady who gave the Club — and the hospital — its name. Mrs. Gilliland made one of her last public appearances at Le Bonheur, and her words were as inspiring as ever:

We founders are glad to have played even a small part in the great work of this wonderful children's medical center. We just dropped a tiny acorn into the good earth long ago, and it has grown into a mighty oak. We are happy and amazed to behold all the great and good things which Le Bonheur Children's Medical Center has done here. It took several years and lots of effort to get the hospital, but everyone helped us, and it all was fun. At last the hospital was a reality, and we took the keys and tied them to a cluster of balloons to indicate that the doors would never be locked. They would be open to all children in need — any race, any religion. All children in need would be welcome at Le Bonheur Hospital. And we have kept it that way. Let us keep thankful hearts and be inspired to more good works, blessings yet to come, as they have in the past, to this wonderful Le Bonheur Children's Medical Center.

On the occasion of its 65th anniversary in 1988, the Le Bonheur Club purchased a new headquarters building at 1047 Cresthaven.

By 1984, so many Le Bonheur Club members had taken up professional careers that the Club began holding membership meetings in the evening. In 1988, the Club celebrated its 65th birthday by donating more than half a million dollars to the hospital for the first time in its history. That same year, the Club purchased a building and moved its offices to 1047 Cresthaven, where they remain today. The building is dedicated to the memory of former president Beatrice Gerber, who made the purchase possible by bequeathing half her estate to the Club.

In 1984, Le Bonheur participated in its first telethon as part of the Children's Miracle Network Telethon, which follows the format of most telethons by featuring national talent interspersed with local segments. The difference is that all the money raised from each participating city stays in the community and goes directly to the local children's hospital. The first year Le Bonheur participated, it raised $230,000. By 1990, the Telethon was raising more than a million dollars each year for the hospital.

As part of the telethon's promotional efforts, a variety of national celebrities have visited Le Bonheur. "I was a patient service representative during my beginning years at Le Bonheur," recalls Club member Kathy Huggins Greene. "We would take around the clowns from the circus, or Santa Claus at Christmas. When the telethon started, Donnie and Marie Osmond came to visit the children. None of the patients knew who they were, but all of the mothers were absolutely screaming."

In 1985, the John Malmo advertising agency was enlisted to help tell the people of Memphis just how unique Le Bonheur is. The result won awards from the Memphis Advertising Federation and was hailed by *The Commercial Appeal* as "the best advertising campaign in Memphis." In an animated television commercial, a child named Margaret visits an adult hospital and finds that "this bed is too big, this gown is too big, and that needle is *way* too big!" She then visits Le Bonheur, where everything is "just right" for children. By turning Margaret into a modern-day Goldilocks, Malmo subtly pointed out the advantages of a facility specially designed for pediatric healthcare.

Margaret quickly become the hospital's mascot, showing up almost everywhere. Local candymaker Dinstuhl's even sold chocolate Margarets as a fundraiser for the hospital. When the Le Bonheur Club made Margaret dolls available in the Bunny Room, they quickly became the most-requested toy. "We've already had a former patient write our club saying that she still had her Margaret doll and wondered if we had one she could give her daughter," says Laurie Monypeny, 1997-98 Club President. "Of course we found one for her."

Margaret was soon joined by her brother Matthew and friends Maryanne and Marcus. Today, nearly twenty years later, these characters are still seen on Le Bonheur materials.

The 1983-84 Le Bonheur Club officers were (left to right) Shirley Browne, President; Jo Anne Tilley, Recording Secretary; J. J. Doughtie, Assistant Treasure; Roseanne Painter, 2nd VP; Betty Pyeatt, 1st VP. Not pictured: Ann Clark Harris, Treasurer and Ginger Patterson, Corresponding Secretary.

The chairmen of the Le Bonheur Club's major fundraising projects in 1985 were (left to right) Ginger Patterson and Gail Kimball, U.S. Indoor Tennis Events; Sally Holmes, Memphis Tags; Evelyn Gotten, Fund Drive; Ginger Owings, Memphis Tags; and Donna Rhodes, Fund Drive.

While the Nation Watches

Le Bonheur's tradition of staying on the cutting edge of healthcare continued with the introduction of an organ transplant program in the early 1980s. The earliest cases brought national media attention to the hospital.

The local and national print media followed the transplant stories.

Diane Sawyer reports on a Le Bonheur transplant case in 1983.

John Donica, Le Bonheur's director of public relations, answers questions for the media.

Above: Media trucks line up outside the hospital.

Below: Le Bonheur physicians hold a press conference in the glare of television lights.

Above and below: Liver transplant recipient Brandon Hall and his mother appear on a national newscast.

What a Doll!

In 1985, Le Bonheur introduced a new mascot named Margaret, who soon became the hospital's "spokesmodel" on everything from bumper stickers (right) to t-shirts (below right). She was later joined by her brother Matthew and friends Maryanne and Marcus (bottom right). Today, nearly twenty years later, these characters continue to represent Le Bonheur.

Le Bonheur is just right.

Above: The ladies of the Le Bonheur Club stuffed and sewed the Margaret dolls that became so popular with Le Bonheur patients as a result of the hospital's animated television commercial.

Below: Showing off the new Margaret dolls in 1985 are (left to right) Linda Wimmer and Sharon McCall, Sewing Club co-chairs; Sandy Sherman, 1985-86 Club President; and Betty Pyeatt, 1984-85 Club President.

Le Bonheur East Night Clinic For Sick Kids

Pediatricians On Duty
6:00 p.m. -11:00 p.m.
Every Night of the Year
No Appointment Necessary.

Le Bonheur EAST

Miracle Stories

In 1984, Le Bonheur joined the Children's Miracle Network Telethon, a star-studded telethon raising money for children's hospitals across the nation.

Right: Le Bonheur president Gene Cashman helps man the phones during the Telethon.

Far right: Le Bonheur public relations director John Donica (right) plans a segment with WREG weatherman Brian Teigland during the hospital's first telethon in 1984, which originated from the Mid-South Fairgrounds.

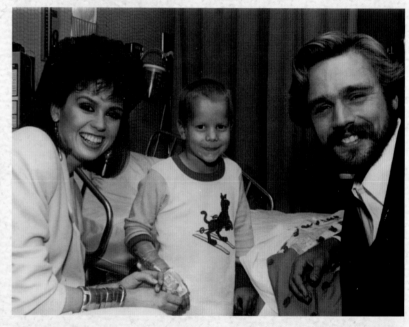

Right: The national portion of the telethon often originates from Disney World.

Far right: National hosts Marie Osmond and John Schneider visit patients in Le Bonheur.

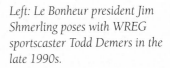

Left: Le Bonheur president Jim Shmerling poses with WREG sportscaster Todd Demers in the late 1990s.

Below: Channel 3's Alex Coleman accepts a donation from a local company.

Above: Singer Donny Osmond, Le Bonheur transplant patient Louis Ragsdale, and WREG's Brian Teigland hold a press conference to promote the 1984 telethon.

Far left: Jerry Tate reviews his notes during the hospital's second telethon in 1985, which was broadcast from the Mall of Memphis.

Left: WREG anchor Pam McCelvy visits a Le Bonheur patient.

Gold Tags

The sale of "Gold Tag" bumper stickers bearing the Le Bonheur logo and the current year has long been a favorite fundraising project of the Le Bonheur Club.

Congressman Dan Kuykendall and his family display the 1967 Gold Tag on their car in Washington, D.C.

MRS. P. M. WATSON

* * *

Tags Boost Hospital

Le Bonheur to Sell 'Memphis' Plates

Le Bonheur Club will sponsor the sale of these city plates, the ... e color as state licenses and ... attachment...

February 1955 article from the Memphis Press-Scimitar.

Sally Hergenrader and Jo Anne Tilley display the 1981 Gold Tags.

1983 Le Bonheur Club president Pat Klinke presents a Gold Tag to Governor Lamar Alexander.

Enchanting

Since the early 1980s, Le Bonheur's neighborhood TWIGS groups have banded together to produce the Festival of Trees, in which corporations sponsor and decorate beautiful Christmas trees as the centerpiece for a weeklong holiday festival. In 1990, Goldsmith's department stores donated the "Enchanted Forest" figures that had fascinated Memphis children for almost fifty years. Renamed the "Enchanted Forest Festival of Trees," the event now runs from Thanksgiving through New Year's, attracts more than 70,000 people, and raises more than $150,000 each year.

Famous Faces at Le Bonheur

Thanks in part to the Children's Miracle Network Telethon, patients at Le Bonheur in the 1980s got to meet more celebrities, heroes, and cartoon characters-come-to-life than ever before.

Sesame Street's Bert and Ernie visit Le Bonheur in 1989 while on tour with Sesame Street Live.

Bugs Bunny pays a visit to promote the Six Flags amusement parks.

Astronaut James Lovell, the first man to make two trips to the moon.

Above: Little Orphan Annie, in town to star in her Broadway musical "Annie" at The Orpheum Theatre, visits Le Bonheur.

Right: Boxing legend Muhammed Ali visits Le Bonheur in 1982.

Below: Blue Angels Jim Davis and Kevin Lauver meet Patrick Jaynes, 7, and Michael Jaynes, 10, in 1988.

1984 Miss Tennessee Moira Kaye visits with 6-year-old Jennifer Riley of Memphis.

The affiliation of the Children's Miracle Network Telethon with Disney World has brought a variety of Disney characters to Le Bonheur.

Far left: Tennis legend Jimmy Connors presents a check to Le Bonheur president Gene Cashman for funds raised by the annual tennis tournament.

Left: Beach Boys Bruce Johnson and Mike Love sign autographs for fans at Le Bonheur.

Below: Singer Crystal Gayle gets a tour of Le Bonheur in 1982.

Dr. Russell Chesney

Below: The Le Bonheur Management Team in 1988. Front row, left to right: David Stevens, Vice President of Professional Services; Gene Cashman, President; Donna Abney, Vice President of Marketing; and Ben Kelly, Vice President of Development. Back row, left to right: Dr. Fred Barrett, Medical Director; Larry Bryan, Vice President of Finance; Dr. Hank Herrod, Vice President of Medical Affairs; Dr. Russell Chesney, Vice President of Academic Affairs; Lenon Coleman, Vice President of Human Resources; and Tim Parris, Chief Operating Officer.

Restructuring

In 1987, Le Bonheur's medical director, John Griffith, left to take a position with Georgetown University. Since 1976, Le Bonheur's medical director had also been the chairman of the UT Department of Pediatrics, but with the increasing workload and new complexities of healthcare management, the job was now divided into three separate positions. Dr. Fred Barrett became Le Bonheur's third medical director. Dr. Hank Herrod was appointed to the newly created position of Vice President of Medical Affairs, which automatically made him vice chairman of the UT Department of Pediatrics. The chairman of the department would become Vice President of Academic Affairs at Le Bonheur. In January 1988, Dr. Russell Chesney was recruited from the University of California at Davis to fill that position.

"I arrived here in late 1987 and was chosen as the chairman by the University," says Chesney. "I really liked the leadership here. I liked the vision they had for the future and it was clear to me that the environment here was going to support child health issues and child health research in a way that really no other place has."

"The kids have directly benefited from this relationship between a private children's hospital and the university," says Dr. Hank Herrod, "and it works better here than it does in almost any place in the country that I'm aware of."

"When I have traveled to seminars and workshops, I have been so pleased to realize that Le Bonheur is one of the top pediatric hospitals in the country," says Margie Whitney, R.N., Nursing Director (retired). "When you're at home you don't see that, but when you go out and talk to other people, you find that we do give top-notch delivery here."

As former board chairman Jane Jones reminds us, "The care of children is different from the care of adults. It is more expensive and it takes people with particular knowledge, so you've got to have people who are dedicated to pediatric care to provide a good place for children. I think Le Bonheur has done it."

CHAPTER FIVE

From Adolescence to Adulthood

By 1990, Memphis was a thriving city with nearly one million inhabitants in its metropolitan area. The revitalization of downtown had been a success. Memphians in 1990 could work in new downtown office buildings like the Morgan Keegan Tower, live in new upscale homes on the south bluffs or in Harbor Town, take a monorail to Mud Island to hear a concert under the stars, and view important historical artifacts through the highly successful *Wonders* cultural series at the Cook Convention Center.

The rebirth of downtown Memphis would continue throughout the 1990s, with the opening of the Pyramid Arena, the National Civil Rights Museum, and a trolley system that carried passengers up and down the length of Main Street Mall. The decade would see growth in other parts of the city, as well. The Children's Museum would open in the old National Guard Armory in 1991, the Wolfchase Galleria mall would stimulate suburban growth starting in 1997, and the new Central Library would be under construction on Poplar by 1999.

By the time of Le Bonheur's 50th birthday in 2002, the city's new Triple-A baseball team, the Memphis Redbirds, would be playing in AutoZone Park. The old Ellis Auditorium would be replaced with the modern Cannon Center for the Performing Arts, Peabody Place shopping and entertainment complex would be open, and major-league sports would finally come to town in the form of an NBA team called the Memphis Grizzlies.

By the 1990s, the Bunny Room had a wider selection of toys, but it continued to play the same pivotal role in easing children's fears before surgery.

Like Memphis, Le Bonheur was moving onward and upward, thanks mainly to the success of its new organizational structure. In 1990, parent company Le Bonheur Health Systems, Inc. moved to new offices at 850 Poplar. The following year, thirty-seven-year-old Jim Shmerling became the hospital's new COO, and in 1995 he became its president. Originally from Nashville, Shmerling had helped run children's hospitals in Indiana and Alabama. The son of a doctor and a pediatric nurse and the father of four, he was well-suited to carry Le Bonheur into the new millennium.

"Le Bonheur has always had a reputation of being innovative amongst children's hospitals around the country," Shmerling says. "Things that Le Bonheur has been doing for ten or twelve years are just now being started in other children's hospitals. The most unique element in Le Bonheur — and I've been in three children's hospitals now — has been the focus on the child rather than on the hospital. In my opinion, Le Bonheur's creativity and its focus on the child put it way out ahead of all the children's hospitals in the country."

A former car dealership at the corner of Poplar and Dunlap, one block north of Le Bonheur, was remodeled to serve as the offices of the hospital's parent company, Le Bonheur Health Systems, Inc.

Reaching Full Maturity

In the five years from 1983 to 1987, annual admissions at Le Bonheur had increased by almost half. It was becoming apparent that it was time for Le Bonheur to grow once again. A $75 million master facilities plan was developed that included several different projects.

In March 1988, renovations began on a former car dealership at Poplar and Dunlap to serve as the administrative offices of Le Bonheur Health Systems, Inc., the parent organization. The new facility at 850 Poplar also housed such hospital departments as Human Resources, Security, the Employee Credit Union, the Business Office, Materials Administration, Accounting, Marketing, Public Relations, Development and the Maintenance shops.

In October 1989, a new 16,000 square-foot, state-of-the-art Emergency Department opened. At the time, it was the largest emergency department and trauma unit in the Mid-South and the only one especially designed and equipped for pediatric patients. "Le Bonheur is the only medical facility in the region staffed 24 hours a day with skilled physicians who are trained in pediatric emergency medicine and capable of handling the special problems of infants and adolescents," said Dr. Joseph Weinberg, Director of Emergency Services. In 1990, a new 20-bed Intensive Care Unit opened, the region's largest pediatric ICU.

Jim Shmerling came to Le Bonheur as chief operating officer in June 1991. In 1995 he would become president.

In October 1991, a new five-story Physicians Office Building was completed on the west side of Dunlap. Connected to the hospital by an underground tunnel and adjacent to Le Bonheur's new four-story parking garage, the 118,000 square-foot office building allowed better outpatient access in a more relaxed environment. "The Physicians Office Building now is a really nice building," says Dr. Robert Hollabaugh, whose offices are located there. "It's very accessible to the hospital. By moving, we were able to get a larger office for the people that needed it, and that was a plus. There's no way they could've done this in the hospital."

Then, on January 6, 1992, the original four-story patient tower built in 1952 was torn down by a 3,000 wrecking ball to make way for the hospital's new seven-story tower. Completed in the summer of 1993, the new tower features a five-story

Here We Grow Again

In the early 1990s, Le Bonheur embarked upon its most ambitious building project to date. As these architectural renderings show, the result would be the culmination of the dream of a truly comprehensive children's medical center. A new seven-story patient tower replaced the original four-story patient wing built in 1952, and the hospital's main entrance was moved to Dunlap Avenue (top photo). Across the street, a new parking garage made room for a four-story Physicians Office Building (bottom photo), which was connected to the main hospital by a pedestrian tunnel under Dunlap.

Above: Before construction began, the space on the west side of Dunlap between Adams and Washington was used mainly for hospital parking. The small building in the foreground was the Le Bonheur Annex, which housed administrative staff. On the opposite end of the block was the Center for Children in Crisis.

Right: The new Physicians Office Building rises behind the Le Bonheur Annex, which was then torn down.

The 118,000-square-foot Physicians Office Building includes a four-level parking garage. The building is connected to the main hospital by a pedestrian tunnel running under Dunlap Avenue.

Top: On January 6, 1992, a 3,000-pound wrecking ball was used to demolish the original four-story patient wing built in 1952.

Above: Dr. James Etteldorf and Dr. James Hughes usher in a new era for the hospital they helped establish.

Top left: The lights at the top of the columns in the new five-story atrium lobby slowly change colors, pulsing out into the starlight pattern on the ceiling.

Top right: Child-friendly artwork is incorporated into the very walls of the hospital.

Center left: Just as it was in the hospital's original design, the cafeteria is found just inside the lobby entrance.

Center right: The Gift Shop continues to be operated by Le Bonheur Club volunteers.

Left: The hospital's diorama now features modern playground equipment for the children.

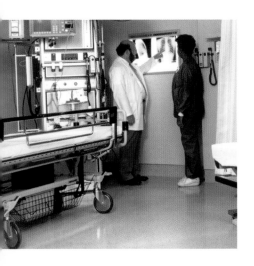

When it opened in October 1989, Le Bonheur's new emergency department and trauma unit was the largest in the Mid-South.

atrium lobby accented with alternating blue, rose, and teal neon lighting. Architect J. Wise Smith describes the sensation: "As the lights pulse to the ceiling, we have what we call 'Van Gogh's Starry Night Pattern' on the ceiling in fiber optics. So, if blue is the last color at the top of the column, then the blue traces all the way out into the ceiling and then the next color is right behind it. We have won a lot of awards for that space. We've made the cover of *Architectural Record*; we made the cover of *Asian Hospital*. So, it has been widely promoted and widely received."

In addition to the atrium, neon lighting is used throughout the new facility to provide a whimsical, less frightening environment for patients. Children's artwork is incorporated into the very walls. "We knew that we wanted the hospital to be childlike but not childish," says Smith. "We found this artist in town who works primarily in ceramics, named Trish Hardy. Trish's little stylistic animals and birds and stuff were absolutely perfect. They were very loose and fun and when she changed them up, she'd take a bird and put specks on it, just purple dots. It was just really great fun, interesting kind of artwork."

The new facility opened in January 1994 with a ribbon-cutting ceremony, reception, and tours for Le Bonheur Club members and other supporters.

Nineties Notes:
Le Bonheur Physicians

Dr. Phil George (third from left) is presented with an oil portrait upon his retirement in 1990. With him are (left to right) artist Paul Penczner, President Gene Cashman, Dr. Russell Chesney, Chairman of the Department of Pediatrics, and Dr. Hank Herrod, Vice President of Medical Affairs.

In 2001, Dr. Stephanie Storgion became Le Bonheur's first female Medical Director.

Dr. Hank Herrod was named Dean of the UT Medical School in 1998.

Dr. Fred Barrett served as Medical Director from 1986 until his retirement in 2001.

Dr. William Novick, pediatric cardiovascular surgery.

Pediatrican Dr. Gerald Presbury.

Dr. George Burghen, pediatric endorcrinology.

Dr. Rick Boop, pediatric neurosurgeon.

Dr. Norman Noe, pediatric urology.

Dr. Robert Sanford, pediatric neurosurgeon.

Private pediatrician Robert Riikola, M.D.

Dr. Webster Riggs, pediatric radiology.

Dr. Mike Quasney, critical care physician.

138

UT Pediatric Residency Program, Le Bonheur Children's Medical Center 1994

First row (left to right): Eniko Pivnick, Jeff Thompson, Martha Miller, Robert Schoumacher, John Eshun, Derrick Hamilton, Rachel Brown, Josh McCollum, Russell Chesney, Barbara Summers, David Kube, Mark Bugnitz, Shane Roy, Hsiao Lai, Sara Zaleta. Second row: Betina Ault, Sharon Snapp, Kevin Stamps, Tracie Overbeck, Scott Stadalsky, Jewel Ward, Ibrahim Sultan-Ali, Nadeem Shafi, Merrick McMains, David Saudek, Cindy Saudek, Stephanie Storgion, Linda Laar, Mark Greenwell. Third row: Tara Houston, Sara Stender, Mary Kline, Kelly Jefferson, John Devincenzo, Valerie Davis, Robert Campbell, Teresa Fritts, Christ Frost, Shane Scott, Colleen Hastings, Laura Winkeler, Natascha Stone, Ty Sullivan, Peggy O'Cain, Dan Duzan, Brent Rosser. Fourth row: Honor Canon, Heather Thompson, Kenya Lee, David Johnston, Maria Streck, Radha Gandi, Molly Hood, Chip Tutor, John Whitworth, Cheri Carrington, Aaron Chen, Heather Dodson, Kelly Kriwanek, Doug Boertje, Angela Redmond, Bonnie Fry, Kacie Lutz, Tracy Flower, Eric Escue. Fifth/Back row: Fred Palmer, Keith Owen, Jara Best, Amrita Dosanjh, Gerald Presbury, Regina Reynolds, Mario Petersen, Gil Herron, Eric Potter, Eddie Thomas, Peter McHugh, Amanda Barre, Judy Wood, Mitch Pullias, Rana Assfoura, Michael Simpson, David Haseltine, Cindy Sands.

UT Pediatric Residency Program, Le Bonheur Children's Medical Center 2002

First row (left to right): Joan Chesney, Elisa Benaim, Rima Jibaly, Anita Durham, Ayesha Shah, Cathy Tsai, Debbie Nelson, Steven Barron, Lisa Anderson, Ayesha Shabbir Dar, Mary Beth Huggins, Art Huggins, Augusta Mayfield. Second row: Shazia Hussain, Walid Salhab, Marcie Castleberry, Randy Denton, Greg Hanissian, Laurie Hult, Becky Raby, Melanie Hoppers, Kim Jones. Third row: Mona Choueiry, Karen Orman, Carol Lynn Colianese, Steve Winbery, John DiMichele, Toni Whitaker, Chris Hanson, Stephanie Shults, Angie Smith-Slack, Gary McBride, Amy Bentley. Fourth row: Russell Chesney, John Kidd, Sam Bartle, Scott Kloek, Syed Amer, Muhammad Ilyas, Philip Kum-Nji, Joe Boals, Barry Crabtree. Fifth/Back row: Rush Waller, Larry Thorne, Kent Nastasi, Scott Whitby, Haysam Baho, Dean Broom, Richard West, Obaid Siddiqui, Keith Tolar, Shripad Banavali, Lea Davis, David Richardson.

Nineties Notes:
Le Bonheur Employees

Patient Care Assistant Lue Brown was Le Bonheur's 1991 Employee of the Year.

Dowtin Martin, Director of Ambulatory Services.

Marlene Shelton, Director of Social Work.

Jan LaBeause, Medical Librarian, December 1990 Employee of the Month.

Joe Green was the 1992 Employee of the Year.

In 1990, Jane Hanafin was named Director of Registration for the Admissions & Emergency Departments.

Andy Fowler, Chief Information Officer.

Amy Todd, Regional Representative, Development Department.

Frank Tamboli, Engineering, was the June 1992 Employee of the Month.

Left: The winners of the volleyball tournament celebrate at the 1990 Employee Picnic.

Below: Linda Lathon, Specimen Control Clerk in the Laboratory, worked 1,825 days without a day off. In July 1991, she was selected as Le Bonheur's Employee of the Month.

Paul Hollahan, Director of Development.

Phyllis Gatlin, Administration, was the August 1992 Employee of the Month.

Oscar West, Security, was Employee of the Month for March 1990.

Inell Allen was the December 1990 Employee of the Month.

In 1990, Janet Lucchesi was promoted to Director of Neurosciences Services.

Kim Margolis, Director of Developmental Pediatrics, Ambulatory Services.

Scott Fowler, Education Production Coordinator, was Employee of the Month in August 1990.

Carolyn McCormick joined the Development Department in 1990.

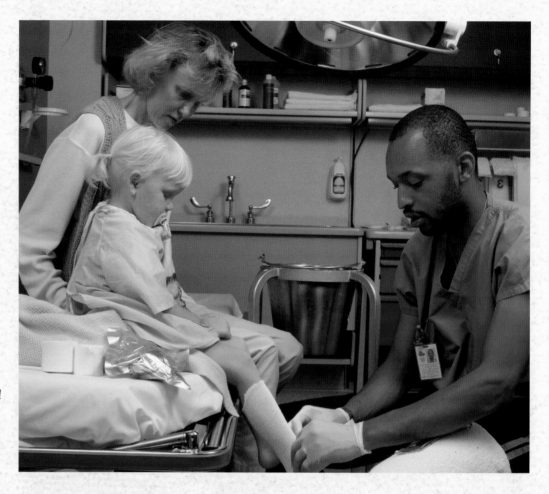

Roderick Davis, Emergency Department Technician, applies a cast to a three-year-old in one of two new suture and cast rooms in Le Bonheur's new 16,000-square-foot Emergency Department, which opened in October 1989.

Louise Spencer, Nurse Associate in the Special Care Unit, was Employee of the Month in April 1998.

Tracy Dunaway, Quality Review, was the December 1996 Employee of the Month.

Kristy Gibbons, Clinical Dietitian, was Employee of the Month for January 1997.

Ester Williams was Employee of the Month for October 1996.

Marianne Walters was the May 1997 Employee of the Month.

Perlandus Harris was the February 1998 Employee of the Month.

Douglas Malone, Nuclear Medicine Technician.

Denise Norman, Psychological Services, was Employee of the Month for November 1997.

Gail French (far left) and Virginia Gibson (left) have given more years of continuous service to Le Bonheur boards than anyone else.

Gail French, who was Le Bonheur Club president in 1980-81, served on the board of Le Bonheur Children's Medical Center from 1980 to 1986. She then joined the board of Le Bonheur Health Systems, Inc., where she served through 2004, giving her 24 years of continuous service.

Virginia Gibson, who was Le Bonheur Club president in 1981-82, served on the board of Le Bonheur Children's Medical Center from 1979 to 1990. She also served on the board of Le Bonheur Health Systems, Inc. from 1983 until 2002, giving her 23 years of continuous service.

Lewis Guy, Environmental Services, was the July 1989 Employee of the Month.

Charlene Somerall was the July 1997 Employee of the Month.

Sonja Hawlins, seen here in the 1990s, had been Employee of the Month in Nov. 1986.

Gene Norris, Access Control Technician, was Employee of the Month in October 1992.

Leroy Woods, Surgery, was the February 1997 Employee of the Month.

Ester Patrick, Unit Secretary, Surgery, was Employee of the Month for January 1998.

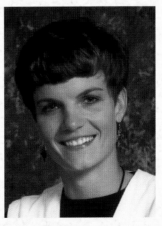

Leslie Robilio, Recovery Room, was Employee of the Month for June 1997.

Evelyn Young, HIM Coordinator, was Employee of the Month in April 1997.

Nineties Notes:
Why We're Here

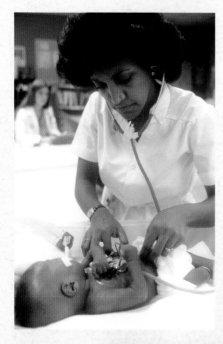

Top left: Chase Crosby of Cordova shows us that the Little Red Wagon is still a mainstay at Le Bonheur.

Middle right: Harrison Devazier of Caldwell, Arkansas enjoys the newly renovated Bunny Room in 2001.

Right: Ryan Scheirholz is head over heels about the new Tender Care Unit, where he was one of the first patients.

Far left: Ruth Eubanks, R.N., Emergency Department, uses freezer pops to bring a smile to a young patient's face in 1998.

Left and below: Volunteers play an important role at Le Bonheur.

Middle left: Physical therapist Mary Pat Jobes assists a patient going through rehabilitation in 1992.

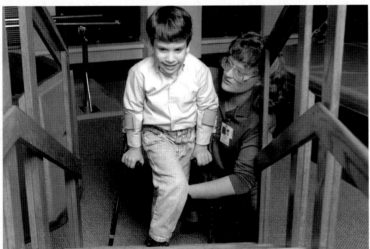

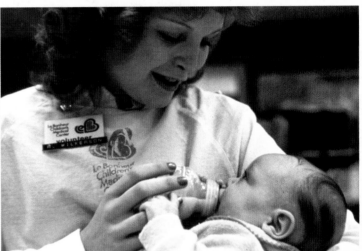

Every Child Needs a Parent

Back in 1981, when the board of directors of Le Bonheur commissioned a long-range strategic plan from M. Bostin & Associates, they were told that the hospital might not be able to permanently remain an independent, freestanding institution. After all, most children's hospitals had always been connected to medical universities or to adult hospitals. The Bostin report explored a variety of alternatives. Among them:

> *Consider the development of a formalized relationship with the Methodist and/or Baptist Hospital System(s) as the exclusive institution for pediatric care within either or both System(s).*

As time passed, several factors increased the desirability of such an option. Le Bonheur's indigent patient load, which had only become significant with the closing of Tobey Hospital in 1977, continued to increase. Then, beginning in 1995, Tennessee's new TennCare program further limited reimbursement for indigent patients. In the meantime, the emergence of HMOs and PPOs was putting further restrictions on reimbursement and even threatening to lock Le Bonheur out of significant patient groups.

As then-Vice President of Marketing Donna Abney explains, "When TennCare came into existence and fifty percent of Le Bonheur's world reverted to managed care, we got jolted into what the future was going to be like — reduced utilization, less pay for the services that we render — and it wasn't hard to forecast how difficult it was going to be for Le Bonheur to stay independent." Le Bonheur president Jim Shmerling agrees: "We were too small to maintain our mission of taking all children regardless of their ability to pay and remain financially stable."

Both Methodist and Baptist had developed region-wide, multi-hospital systems. Both systems had considerable financial resources, significant facilities, and management expertise. A formal partnership with either of these systems would allow for the development and expansion of programs that would keep Le Bonheur forever on the forefront of pediatric care in the Mid-South.

"It was a very painful process to go through," says Abney, "and it took us, as a management team, a while to one day say, 'It is the right thing to do.' But, once we all saw that vision and saw that we really could hand the torch off to the next generation to ensure that children in Memphis got the very best care, it became very easy."

LeBonheur, Methodist announce merger plan

LeBonheur Health Systems, Inc. (LHS) Tuesday announced its intent to merge LeBonheur Children's Medical Center, Inc., with Methodist Health Systems, Inc. (MHS). An agreement has been signed and closing is expected to be complete by October 1, 1995. Both the LeBonheur and Methodist Boards of Directors have endorsed the merger plans.

"The Board and management of Methodist have demonstrated their commitment to children's health care and the LeBonheur mission. We feel a strong sense of compatibility with their culture and vision," said Eugene K. Cashman, Jr., President and Chief Executive Officer, LHS, Inc.

At the center of the merger is a comprehensive women and children's initiative designed to serve the entire Mid-South. Included in the plan will be the expansion of the LeBonheur Cordova Urgent Care Center and development of LeBonheur ser at Methodist Germantown.

"LeBonheur brings to Methodist a depth of pediatric expertise which is unparalleled in the region. We are excited at the opportunity to play a role in enhancing LeBonheur's mission while at the same time further developing Methodist's goal of an integrated health care delivery system," said Maurice Elliott, President and Chief Executive Officer, MHS, Inc.

Linkages have been a long-standing strategy for LHS. Discussions with many different systems have taken place in an attempt to seek out alternative means by which to continue to deliver high quality, low cost pediatric care.

"Merger talks have taken into account the ways in which health care delivery is changing. Our _ goal is to gua___ viab'''

feels strongly that its position with Methodist will ensure that goal for the future," said Cashman.

"MHS and LHS are working toward a common vision on how to serve the health care needs of the people of Memphis and the greater Mid-South community, including the needs of children," said Elliott.

A key component in all talks has been open access to LeBonheur services for all children.

"Any child in this region who needs the level of care which only LeBonheur and its affiliated physicians and pediatric experts can deliver will get it. In fact, we expect this merger to enhance that throughout ___

Signing the final documents for the Methodist/Le Bonheur merger are (seated, left to right) Maurice Elliot, President and Chief Executive Officer, Methodist Health Systems; Eugene K. Cashman, Jr., Chief Executive Officer, Le Bonheur Health Systems, Inc.; Gary Shorb, President and Chief Executive Officer, Methodist Hospitals of Memphis; (standing, left to right) Steve West, Senior Vice President, Legal Affairs, Methodist Health Systems; and Bob Trumpis, Senior Vice President, Methodist Health Systems.

Le Bonheur CFO Robert Trimm says, "One of the things that was really positive to me consistently throughout the whole Le Bonheur experience is that I never saw people get too concerned about, 'What does it mean to me?' I saw a whole lot more concern about doing what was best long-term."

The Le Bonheur management team made cautious overtures to their competitors. "Our first choice," says Cashman, "was to develop a community model with Baptist and Methodist where the two big systems and Le Bonheur would share equity and the pediatric care in this community. We floated that to the two big systems. It was rejected, so we went to option two, which was a joint venture with one of the two big systems."

When efforts to negotiate a joint venture failed, the only option left was a merger. Methodist showed the most interest. "We were very interested," says Gary Shorb, CEO of Methodist Healthcare. "We were committed to staying downtown and to serving the entire community. We were committed to ensuring that pediatric care remained high quality for the entire community."

"With Methodist we found a corporate culture enormously similar to ours," says Abney. "Very qualitative in the way they go about decision-making."

"They recognized our expertise, they recognized their shortfall in pediatrics and anticipated what kind of a market advantage they would have in having a strong pediatric program as part of their service," says Shmerling. "In making the decision when we did, we were able to negotiate from a position of strength. And ultimately, in six months the contract had been signed in the merger with Methodist."

The merger between Methodist Health Systems and Le Bonheur Children's Medical Center occurred in October of 1995. The resulting organization became the largest healthcare employer in the region. With that, a loop was closed that began in 1941, when the Le Bonheur Club opened the city's first free medical clinic for children in the old Methodist Hospital Building.

Both organizations made a pledge that no employee would be laid off as a result of the merger. In fact, the merger actually created some jobs. For example, in January 1996, Sue Beverly joined Le Bonheur as director of Clinical Pastoral Education/Chaplain, the first full-time chaplain in the hospital's history. In the past, Le Bonheur staff had called on community clergy to assist in spiritual matters.

Le Bonheur CFO Robert Trimm played a pivotal role in the merger of Methodist and Le Bonheur.

Art therapy remains an important part of Le Bonheur's commitment to treat "the whole child." And what could be more fun than being allowed to paint right on the windows of the hospital?

Over time, some positions were consolidated, and some departments — such as development, printing, and physician services — were combined. Services such as the physician referral services were also combined, all without eliminating jobs. The organization even published a separate newsletter called "Merger News" to keep the employees informed and to prevent misinformation from causing apprehension.

When the new partnership was first announced, most people assumed that Le Bonheur would merely be absorbed into the Methodist system, and that the Le Bonheur identity would soon be lost forever. But consumer surveys showed the management of Methodist just how precious Le Bonheur was to the Memphis community. For example, one survey showed that the Le Bonheur logo, without the hospital's name, was recognized by 98 percent of consumers.

As a result, it was always stressed to the public that this was a merger, not an acquisition. No money had changed hands. Le Bonheur was almost always featured in the new organization's advertising, which combined the logos of the two institutions into "Methodist/Le Bonheur." In January 1998, when Methodist Health Systems changed its name to Methodist Healthcare, it made sure to announce that the name of Le Bonheur Children's Medical Center would remain unchanged.

The merger not only strengthened Le Bonheur's overall position in the healthcare marketplace, it also allowed Le Bonheur's expertise in pediatrics to reach the Mid-South through the eleven Methodist hospitals in a three-state region. In January 1996, just three months after the merger took place, a six-bed Le Bonheur pediatric unit opened in Methodist Germantown. By Le Bonheur's 50th birthday in 2002, Jim Shmerling said, "We're working in all of the emergency departments at Methodist, so they are certified to take care of children. We're making sure they have the right size equipment and that the training of the staff, both nursing and physicians, is pediatric-specific." He added that plans for the new Methodist hospital being built in Cordova included a seven-acre Le Bonheur campus.

While Le Bonheur's expertise was carried into the Methodist system, the reverse was also true. For example, in September 1996, a 15-bed pediatric psychiatric unit opened at Le Bonheur as a joint effort with Methodist Behavioral Health. As the only psychiatric unit in the region located within a pediatric medical complex, the unit offers a unique range of services.

The expertise of the larger system was carried over in non-medical areas, as well. "Customer service has always been a focal point of Le Bonheur," says Brenda Garner. "I think that we have a very effective customer service program at Le Bonheur and, I think, one that offers a lot of promise. I think being a part of a larger entity like Methodist has helped us to really focus and to learn different customer service strategies."

Perhaps the best example of the joint efforts to arise out of the merger is the Partnership for Women's and Children's Health, founded in 1996. "The Partnership represents a relationship between Le Bonheur, Methodist Health Systems, and the University of Tennessee," says Dr. Hank Herrod, original director of the program.

"It's mission is to measurably — and that's a key word — improve in a sustained fashion the health and well-being of women and children in Memphis, Shelby County, West Tennessee, and the Mid-South." The Partnership pursues quantifiable goals such as reducing the number of low-weight births in the region to no more than 8 percent of live births, or getting 90 percent of children fully immunized by the age of two.

Following the merger, the former parent company, Le Bonheur Health Systems, Inc., moved to offices out east, and the for-profit subsidiary corporations were sold or dissolved. Since then, Le Bonheur Health Systems, Inc. has become The Urban Child Institute (TUCI). Still under the management of Gene Cashman, TUCI seeks new ways to improve the health and welfare of children throughout the community.

"We are giving grants for children's initiatives in the community," says TUCI board member Gail French. "After all these years of being a part of Le Bonheur hospital and the Club, serving on the grants committee for TUCI is one of the most exciting opportunities I've had. It's thrilling to see how the monies are being used in the community for the enrichment of children's lives."

"The merger with Methodist has allowed Le Bonheur as a pediatric hospital in the Mid-South to survive," says Rosanne Painter, who served as chairman of the hospital board from 1993 to 1995. "Being under the umbrella of a big hospital corporation has let Le Bonheur keep its individuality yet still make it in the world of medicine today."

"The people are working well together," says former Le Bonheur board chairman Dick Trippeer. "The Methodist culture fits well with the Le Bonheur culture. I'm confident that the two organizations are better together than they were apart."

On May 17, 1996, in the midst of the merger with Methodist, an event occurred that seemed to confirm that Le Bonheur's new direction was both a beginning and an ending. Mrs. Elizabeth Jordan Gilliland passed away at the age of 97. Sixty-three years had passed since she had named the club that would later start the hospital, and from which the hospital would take its name. "Mother often said she never dreamed it could be as huge and successful as it has become," said her son, Jim Gilliland, at the time of her death. How could she have dreamed that, in her lifetime, the hospital she named would become part of the largest healthcare system in the region and one of the largest in the world?

In 1991, pediatric therapist Diana Chiles brought Bernard the puppet to Le Bonheur. Bernard, who portrays a patient at the hospital (he even has his own ID wristband), never tires of encouraging children during their stay.

Carrying the Le Bonheur Spirit Into the New Millennium

Despite a major construction project and the merger with Methodist Health Systems, Le Bonheur continued, as usual, to focus its primary attention on finding new ways to help make sick children well and keep them that way.

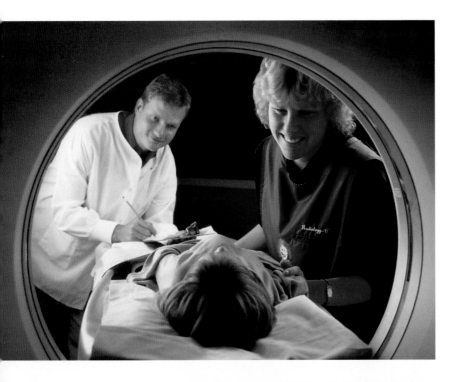

In October 1990, Le Bonheur opened a 6,600-square-foot pediatric imaging center named The Sam Walton Children's CT/MRI Center. This was supplemented in March 1991 by the new 3,800-square-foot Cardiovascular Imaging Lab, placing Le Bonheur on the forefront of imaging capabilities.

In 1992, Le Bonheur became the lead organization for the Mid-South SAFE KIDS Coalition, part of a national campaign to reduce the number of children's injuries, the main health risk facing children today. The Coalition conducted public awareness campaigns on such things as the proper use of seat belts and air bags for children. Beginning in 1996, it published *The Play Smart Holiday Guide to Toy Safety*, which it distributed to low-income families through the MIFA Christmas Store.

Also in 1992, for the first time ever, more than 100,000 children were treated at Le Bonheur on either an inpatient or outpatient basis.

In 1993, a $5 million gift from the Crippled Children's Foundation led to the opening of the Children's Foundation Research Center of Memphis. Within the walls of the Research Center, pediatric investigators from Le Bonheur and the UT Department of Pediatrics work to unravel the mysteries behind childhood illnesses such as asthma, diabetes, arthritis, kidney disease, and cystic fibrosis. The Center combines research activities that were once conducted in seven separate buildings throughout the Memphis Medical Center. By 1996, the Center included 37 specially designed laboratories, allowing pediatric investigators and researchers access to the latest technology and equipment for studying diseases. As Dr. Bob Summitt, Dean of the College of Medicine put it at the time, "Le Bonheur provides a terrific venue for teaching students and for training residents. With the addition of the Children's Foundation Research Center, it has now become the center for the research that is done in pediatrics."

In 1995, the Neurosciences Center for Children and Adolescents was formed, specializing in brain tumors, epilepsy, spinal cord injuries, sleep disorders, and attention and behavioral problems.

In 1997, Le Bonheur formed an unprecedented alliance with the Memphis City Schools to form the Coordinated School Health Program (CSHP). The goal of the CSHP is to produce healthy, well-educated children who will become responsible, productive, employable adults with a high quality of life.

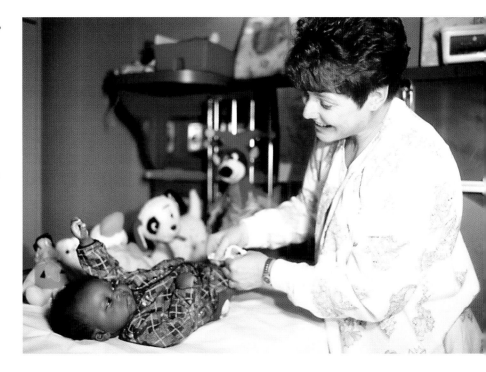

Also in 1997, as a benefit for Le Bonheur, children from throughout the area hand painted more than 1,200 square tiles that were then installed near the carousel at the new Wolfchase Galleria mall, opening at Germantown Parkway and I-40. Parents and other adults purchased the tiles for $40 each, raising nearly $50,000 for the hospital.

In 1998, the first split-liver transplant in the Mid-South region was performed successfully at Le Bonheur and UT Bowld Hospital, Memphis. In May of the same year, Les Passees, a non-profit agency that had provided services to developmentally delayed children since 1949, merged with Le Bonheur. The resulting program, called Le Bonheur Early Intervention and Development (LEAD), was located in Le Bonheur's main building with a staff of 40. LEAD serves mainly Medicaid patients with such afflictions as cerebral palsy, fetal alcohol syndrome, and Downs syndrome.

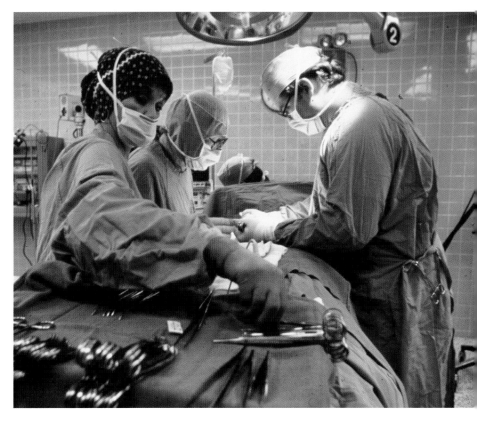

In 2000, the Le Bonheur Center for Children in Crisis, which served families of victims of child abuse and neglect, completed its merger with The Parenting Center, a non-profit agency founded in 1985 to provide support and education to families. The resulting organization, The Le Bonheur Center for Children and Parents, is located at 2400 Poplar Avenue.

In 2001, Le Bonheur received designation from the State of Tennessee as West Tennessee's only Comprehensive Regional Pediatric Center.

In 2002, an endoscopic surgery suite, the first of its kind in the Mid-South, was opened to perform minimally-invasive surgical procedures in children.

Famous Faces at Le Bonheur

Right: In the early 1990s, seven-year-old Jessica Andrews of Huntington, Tennessee came to Le Bonheur so neurosurgeons could correct a congenital spinal cord deformity. In 2000, 17-year-old Jessica (right) topped the country music charts with her song "Who I Am." Following her success, Jessica returned to Le Bonheur (far right) to express her appreciation.

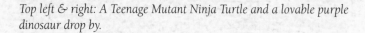

Top left & right: A Teenage Mutant Ninja Turtle and a lovable purple dinosaur drop by.

Above: The Crash Test Dummies visit Le Bonheur in 1993 to promote the SAFE Kids Coalition, a partnership between Le Bonheur, the Tennessee Highway Patrol, and the Memphis & Shelby County Health Department.

Right: All-Pro Houston Oilers quarterback Warren Moon visits Le Bonheur in 1991. Moon was in town for an exhibition game in preparation for the Oilers' move to Tennessee, where they would be renamed the Titans.

Far left: Roger Rabbit joins Mickey and Minnie in visiting Le Bonheur patients.

Left: Actor Gary Busey visited Le Bonheur on behalf of the SAFE Kids Coalition to promote bicycle safety helmets. Busey had suffered serious head injuries in a 1988 motorcycle accident.

Below left: University of Memphis basketball star Penny Hardaway helps raise funds for Le Bonheur in 1995.

Top: Sports legend Bo Jackson supported Le Bonheur through his participation in the Children's Miracle Network Telethon. Jackson had played some of his minor league baseball games in Memphis.

Above: Blues legend B.B. King visits Le Bonheur.

Left: 1992 Miss America Carolyn Sapp.

Fifty Years Young

In 2002, Le Bonheur Children's Medical Center marked its 50th birthday with a year-long celebration. A clever logo designed by The Sossaman Agency incorporated the Le Bonheur logo directly into the word "Celebrate," and an equally clever billboard showed five pairs of children's handprints and proclaimed, "We're this many years old!" Stories were collected from former patients and their parents and published in a special tabloid. A 45-minute video documentary tracing the history of Le Bonheur was made possible by a special gift from the family of Elizabeth Gilliland. The celebrations culminated in a street party and special ceremony at the hospital entrance on June 15th.

During these celebrations, the past, present, and future met in the form of three extraordinary ladies who took part in several of the birthday activities:

- Billie Ann Carrington — first president of the Le Bonheur Club at its founding in 1923, who turned 101 years old in 2002.
- Elise Pritchard — president of the Le Bonheur Club at the hospital's opening in 1952 and the woman who had released the first bunch of balloons bearing the hospital keys.
- And Debbie Edmundson — Le Bonheur Club president during the hospital's 50th anniversary in 2002, 79 years after the ladies of Le Bonheur first started helping the children of Memphis and the Mid-South.

By its 50th year, Le Bonheur had grown from a small but respected children's hospital to a nationally recognized pediatric healthcare center. Le Bonheur in 2002 had 225 beds, 42 pediatric sub-specialty clinics, and a medical staff of more than 550. It served a 95-county referral area that included portions of six states, in which lived nearly one million children. In addition, children were being referred to Le Bonheur from every state and many foreign countries.

"I came to Le Bonheur in October of 1985," says Brenda Garner, Customer Services Manager. "When I started working here we had probably 850 employees. We now have over 1,400 employees."

"We now have a house staff of 84 residents," says Russell Chesney, Vice-President of Academic Affairs, "which is a large med peds program — actually the largest in the country — and a huge involvement of residents coming from medical schools. We currently have residents from 34 U.S. medical schools on our house staff. We've actually trained more pediatricians in this state than any other training program."

The clever theme for Le Bonheur's 50th Birthday celebration was created by The Sossaman Agency.

We're this Many Years old! ce(le)Brate

50 Years Of Loving Kids

LE BONHEUR CHILDREN'S MEDICAL CENTER · 1952 - 2002

Left: Three Extraordinary Ladies:
Elise Pritchard; 1952 Le Bonheur
Club president, Debbie Edmundson,
2002 Le Bonheur Club president;
and Billie Ann Carrington, 1923
Le Bonheur Club president.

Below: Billie Ann Carrington (right),
who was the Club's first president in
1923, with Pat Klinke, who was Club
president sixty years later, in 1983.

"Virtually every pediatrician in town is on staff at Le Bonheur," says Memphis pediatrician Dr. Bob Riikola. "I can't recall anybody who actually is not. Most of us pretty much admit exclusively to Le Bonheur."

"So Le Bonheur has grown from a small, wonderful little hospital to an incredibly powerful, outstanding regional medical center of which we are quite proud," says Gail French. "We have a lot of people who have contributed greatly to the board and to the growth of the hospital, and without them, Le Bonheur would not be where it is today."

"We had wonderful board members over the years who have been very supportive, very active," adds Sallie Foster. "Le Bonheur Club has just been phenomenal. The support from the community, the employees who worked 24 hours a day — if something needed to be done, they were right there."

"We are where we always dreamed we would be," says Jane Jones. "It has taken so many years and so many people to work on it that way, but then, we are doing good work. Let's face it, we are helping children. It gives me a lump in my throat when I think about it, how good it is now and how accepted Le Bonheur is. It really is a dream come true."

ce🗲Brate

50 Years Of Loving Kids

On June 15, 2002, Le Bonheur threw itself a birthday party that featured a parade, games, birthday cake, and speeches by hospital administrators and local government officials.

Longtime Le Bonheur employee Eulila Flinn flanked by Congressman Harold Ford, Jr. and former Le Bonheur president Gene Cashman.

Methodist CEO Gary Shorb and Congressman Harold Ford, Jr.

1952 Le Bonheur Club president Elise Pritchard (center) makes her entrance.

"A Joy Beyond Explaining"

On June 15, 1952, 50 years to the day after the keys to Le Bonheur first floated away into the hot Memphis sky, the Le Bonheur family gathered to celebrate a half century of helping children. On a sunny, breezy Saturday morning, Dunlap Avenue in front of the hospital was closed to traffic. Doctors, nurses, staff, former and current patients, and the founders and supporters of Le Bonheur joined in the grand celebration.

The party kicked off with a parade featuring more than 300 individuals and "floats"— decorated wagons, wheelchairs, strollers, and gurneys carrying current and

former patients past the front of the hospital. Children danced in the streets, played games, and ate birthday cake. The Hospital Wing helicopter passed back and forth overhead while a more-than-lifesized Margaret mascot offered hugs to all takers. A 25-year-old time capsule was opened, revealing historical documents. In the hospital auditorium, a new documentary film recounting the history of Le Bonheur played continuously throughout the day. Hospital administrators and local government officials praised Le Bonheur's contribution to the community and looked forward to an even brighter future.

Then came the moment everyone had been waiting for. Billie Ann Carrington, Elise Pritchard, and Debbie Edmundson — three Le Bonheur Club presidents whose terms spanned 79 years — stood together on the platform and released a new cluster of balloons, symbolizing once again Le Bonheur's continuing commitment to the children of the community. The balloons soared swiftly aloft into the bright blue sky, and Le Bonheur's second fifty years was begun.

"The wonderful things they do here," said Elise Pritchard with a tear in her eye, "well, you can just hardly believe that the little thing we started has grown into something so lovely and big. I just have the feeling of pure joy to have had the opportunity to be a part of something that is continuing in what is a wonderful thing for children. For it to happen is just something that makes you feel good for having started something that continues. There is just a joy there that is beyond explaining."

Le Bonheur. The good hour. The hour of happiness. An idea developed almost eighty years ago by a small group of young women seeking to help the children of their community. Thirty years later, that idea hatched into a small children's hospital. And fifty years after that, Le Bonheur has grown into a premier children's institution and vital community resource.

How many "good hours" have been donated to the children of the Mid-South by the volunteers and staff of Le Bonheur? How many illnesses cured? How many lives saved? No one knows exactly, but one thing is sure: Le Bonheur Children's Medical Center always has — and always will — do "whatever it takes" for the children it serves.

"Le Bonheur is..."

The 50th birthday of an institution like Le Bonheur causes people to reflect on what the hospital has meant to them through the years. We asked a variety of Le Bonheur family members to complete the sentence "Le Bonheur is...." Here's what they had to say:

"Le Bonheur is a place where children get the very best care when they are in need, without regard to their parents' financial circumstances or religious beliefs. Le Bonheur is a safe harbor and the very best place for a sick child to come to."

Donna Abney
Former Le Bonheur VP of Marketing,
Senior Vice President, Methodist Healthcare

"Le Bonheur is a tremendous addition to the community, the medical community, and the city at large."

Newton Allen
Former Le Bonheur Board Member

"Le Bonheur is people taking care of people."

James Aune
Le Bonheur Comptroller
(retired)

"Le Bonheur is a place where pediatricians and medical students can interact and learn what's best about pediatrics."

Russell Chesney, M.D.
Chairman, University of Tennessee
Department of Pediatrics

"Le Bonheur is the place that the highest quality of care for children can be obtained in the Mid-South."

Larry Dormois, D.D.S.
Pediatric Dentist

"Le Bonheur is *the* place for a child to be. A place where a child will get the best care and their family will be looked after. Le Bonheur is a wonderful family. The hospital has and will always have a really special place in my heart — I will always be Le Bonheur."

Sallie Foster
Executive Assistant,
The Urban Child Institute

"Le Bonheur is the greatest hospital for any child, anywhere."

Brenda Garner
Le Bonheur Customer Services
Manager

"Le Bonheur is my heart. I had a brother not with us now, and Le Bonheur had saved his life many, many times. I knew the hospital back when it was very young. I am dedicated to Le Bonheur and the people I work for."

Phyllis Gatlin
Executive Secretary, Le Bonheur

"Le Bonheur is really important to this community and this region, but it serves the nation and the world as a whole — because we have trained so many physicians here who are practicing in other environments."

Phillip George, M.D.
Pediatric Pulmonologist (retired)

"Le Bonheur is one of the city's biggest assets."

Laurie Monypeny
Le Bonheur Club President 1997-98

"Le Bonheur is the place that you need to be if your child is in need. There is no doubt about that."

Susan Helms
Le Bonhuer Director of Injury Prevention

"Le Bonheur is a very special place for kids. There's nothing like it."

Dowtin Martin
Le Bonheur Director of Ambulatory Services

"Le Bonheur is a wonderful place to work. The surgical and pediatric medical staff subspecialties are as good as I've ever seen anywhere and I think the physical plant is as good as you can ask for. I consider it an honor and a pleasure to have been able to work at Le Bonheur."

Robert Hollabaugh, M.D.
Pediatric Surgeon

"Le Bonheur is a leader in the community, particularly in the Southeast, in terms of care of children. The hospital has been progressive in research, service, and in the quality of care. I am proud to have been associated with Le Bonheur."

Fred Nowak
Le Bonheur Senior Vice President (retired)

"Le Bonheur is caring for children. Everyone connected with it, the Club and then the hospital, are dedicated to the premise that they want the very best for children regardless of their ability to pay."

Sue Cheek Hughes
Architect (retired),
Le Bonheur Club Member

"Le Bonheur is helping children from all walks of life."

Roseann Painter
Le Bonheur Board Chairman 1993-95

"Le Bonheur is great. It is a nice place to work. Le Bonheur is the best children's hospital there is. When I came here in 1956 it was a nice place and it still is."

Louise Jackson
Le Bonheur Nutrition Supervisor (retired)

"Le Bonheur is a community treasure. What it has offered over the years since its birth — the expertise, the true focus on caring for the whole child and the entire family — I think that is unduplicated in this community. It is a resource that we all should be very thankful for."

Janet Phillips
Le Bonheur Marketing Director

"Le Bonheur is an outstanding facility, a prize for the city of Memphis."

Ray Paul, M.D.
Pediatric Cardiologist (retired)

"Le Bonheur is an advocate for children in children's health — not just children who are sick, but children in general. The hospital is an advocate for their wellness, an advocate for their rights."

Jim Shmerling
Le Bonheur President 1995-2002

"Le Bonheur is a most unique pediatric teaching and caregiving facility. It's unique in several ways. It has a heart that began back when they formed 'the good hour' and that has never dwindled — that flame has never dwindled or died."

William Rachels, D.D.S.
Former Le Bonheur Board Member

"Le Bonheur is an organization of individuals, all of whom share at least one thing — a passionate love for the welfare of children. Whether that is someone in housekeeping or someone at the upper level of administration, we all share that goal. It creates a very unique ambiance."

Greg Stidham, M.D.
Director, Intensive Care Unit

"Le Bonheur is a tremendous resource for the University of Tennessee. As I have said to many people, it's been one of our best, if not *the* best, hospital relationships that we've had in Memphis, so that's got to be number one with me."

Bill Rice, M.D.
Chancellor, University of Tennessee Health Science Center (retired)

"Le Bonheur is a tremendous resource to the community in its programs in pediatrics and is a tremendous resource to the College of Medicine and to UT beyond the College of Medicine, from the standpoint of education, research, and patient care."

Robert Summitt, M.D.
Dean of the UT College of Medicine (retired)

"Le Bonheur is, in my view, the only place to provide total and complete pediatric care in the city. I have a great affection for the institution since I participated as a resident here and continue to have that same feeling for the institution up until this day."

Robert Riikola, M.D.
Pediatrician

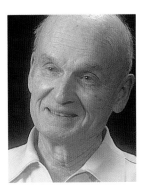

"Le Bonheur is the hospital that I would want my family to be in, then and now, if they were ill."

Price Stepp, M.D.
Pediatrician (retired)

"Le Bonheur is, truly, the angel of mercy. I think that the Lord has a hand in Le Bonheur."

Virginia Sloan
Le Bonheur Nurse (retired)

APPENDICES

Appendix A
Le Bonheur Club Presidents
(and the years they served)

Billie Anthony Carrington (1923 - 1924)

*Marguerite Randolph Turner (1924 - 1925)

*Lucille Berwick Snowden (1925 - 1926)

*Mildred May Elliotte (1926 - 1927)

*Sara Maddux Van Fossan (1927 - 1928)

*Jewell Smith Barwick (1928 - 1929)

*Ada McDonnell Smith (1929 - 1931)

*Jeannette McCormack Reber (1931 - 1932)

*Martha Allen Long (1932 - 1934)

*Gwendolyn Watson Graham (1934 - 1935)

*Mary Chunn Wilkinson Babendreer (1935 - 1936)

*Mary Louise McPhillips Saxon (1936 - 1937)

*Kate Person Land Pritchard (1937 - 1938)

*Mary Catherine Prest Wade (1938 - 1939)

*Margaret Trenholm Moore (1939 - 1940)

*Cornelia Covington Allstadt Gatlin (1940 - 1941)

*Beatrice Scheibler Gerber (1941 - 1942)

*Ada McDonnell Smith (1942 - 1943)

*Peggy Witherington Kimbrough (1943 - 1944)

Margaret Conger Barnett (1944 - 1945)

*Ruth Burton Pidgeon (1945 - 1946)

*Elizabeth Miller Stratton (1946 - 1947)

*Beatrice Scheibler Gerber (1947 - 1949)

*Ruth McClure Curd (1949 - 1950)

*Mary Carolyn Ellis Rabb (1950 - 1951)

Elise Porter Pritchard (1951 - 1952)

*Jean McKneely Weathersby (1952 - 1953)

*Amy Smith Porter (1953 - 1954)

*Martha Baptist DeSaussure Collins (1954 - 1955)

Alice Shangraw Schadt (1955 - 1956)

*Sarah Phillips Crenshaw (1956 - 1957)

*Esther Jones Doughtie Jeffries (1957 - 1958)

*Eugenia Armistead Blanchard (1958 - 1959)

*Mary Ann McCabe Avery (1959 - 1960)

Sue Cheek Smith Hughes (1960 - 1961)

Golda DeCell Minor (1961 - 1962)

Maline Charlton Prest (1962 - 1963)

*Elizabeth Parsons Dudley (1963 - 1964)

*Blenda Olson Heller (1964 - 1965)

Penelope Potts Bailey (1965 - 1966)

Sally Palmer Thomason (1966 - 1967)

Margaret Hooks Wilson (1967 - 1968)

Hylda Hicks Whitman (1968 - 1969)

*Ruth Younghanse Crenshaw (1969 - 1970)

Jane Doles Jones (1970 - 1971)

Betty Goff Cook Cartwright (1971 - 1972)

Lucy Carrington Jones (1972 - 1973)

Terry Kimbrough Brown (1973 - 1974)

Ann Garber Creson Fordice (1974 - 1975)

*Florence Harris Hinson (1975 - 1976)

Billie Anne Beaumont Williams (1976 - 1977)

Mary Louise Rickets Moffatt (1977 - 1978)

Mary Ann Davenport Ford (1978 - 1979)

Margaret Williams Harwell (1979 - 1980)

Gail Little French (1980 - 1981)

Virginia Taylor Buhler Gibson (1981 - 1982)

Patricia Gardner Klinke (1982 - 1983)

Shirley Polk Browne (1983 - 1984)

Betty Hunt Pyeatt (1984 - 1985)

Sandy Sherrod Sherman (1985 - 1986)

Margaret Lott Schaefer (1986 - 1987)

Jo Anne Bratton Tilley (1987 - 1988)

Evelyn Schlafer Gotten (1988 - 1989)

Roseann Harwood Painter (1989 - 1990)

Ann Clark Quinlen Harris (1990 - 1991)

Kate Flowers Weathersby (1991 - 1992)

Glenna Boales Flautt (1992 - 1993)

Beth Baker Breazeale (1993 - 1994)

Clara Dean Cox Hope (1994 - 1995)

Donna Wolfe Rhodes (1995 - 1996)

Libby Reese Aaron (1996 - 1997)

Laurie Parsons Monypeny (1997 - 1998)

Patty Reynolds Johnson (1998 - 1999)

Nancy Powell Kelley (1999 - 2000)

Mary Lawrence Hughes Flinn (2000 - 2001)

Debbie Nix Edmundson (2001 - 2002)

Susan Hoskins Razzouk (2002 - 2003)

Deceased (as of December 31, 2002)

Appendix B
Chairmen, Board of Directors
Le Bonheur Children's Hospital/Medical Center, Inc.
(and the years they served)

*J. Everett Pidgeon (1952, 1953)

*Thurston Roach (1954, 1955)

*Norman Isenberg (1956)

*Thomas D. Bell (1957, 1958)

*Downing Pryor (1959, 1960)

*Eugene J. Pidgeon (1961, 1962)

Ed Jappe (1963)

*Paul Borda (1964, 1965, 1966, 1967)

W. H. Rachels, D.D.S. (1968, 1969, 1970, 1971, 1972)

*George Phillips (1972)

Mrs. Robert K. Jones (Jane) (1973, 1974, 1975, 1976)

Richard A. Trippeer, Jr. (1977, 1978, 1979)

Joe H. Davis, Jr. (1980, 1981)

J. Fraser Humphreys, Jr. (1982, 1983)

Frank A. Jones (1984)

Donald F. Schuppe (1985, 1986)

John S. Collier (1987, 1988)

Mrs. John V. M. Gibson (Virginia) (1989, 1990)

Donald F. Schuppe (1991, 1992, 1993)

Mrs. Max W. Painter (Roseann) (1994, 1995)

David Rhodes (1996, 1997)

Ronald Walter (1998, 1999)

Emile Bizot, III (2000, 2001)

Steve Wishnia (2002, 2003)

Deceased (as of December 31, 2002)

Appendix C
Administrators/Presidents
Le Bonheur Children's Hospital/Medical Center, Inc.
(and the years they served)

1. Freeman E. May (July 1951 - April 1954)
2. Adalbert G. Dierks (May 17, 1954 - November 1963)
3. Donald C. McGrath (January 1964 - March 1968)
4. Charles W. Bradley (April 1968 - April 1977)
5. Eugene K. Cashman, Jr. (November 1977 - October 1995)
6. James E. Shmerling (October 1995 - June 2002)

Appendix D
Medical Directors
Le Bonheur Children's Hospital/Medical Center, Inc.
(and the years they served)

1. *James G. Hughes, M.D.
   (September 1972 - December 1975)
2. John F. Griffith, M.D. (July 1976 - 1986)
3. Fred Barrett, M.D. (July 1986 - 2000)
4. Stephanie Storgion, M.D. (2001 -   )

Appendix E
Chairmen, Department of Pediatrics
University of Tennessee
(and the years they served)

1. *E. Clay Mitchell, M.D. (1936 - 1940)
2. *Tom Mitchell, M.D. (1940 - 1960)
3. *James Hughes, M.D.(1960 - 1976)
4. John F. Griffith, M.D. (1976 - 1986)
5. Henry G. Herrod, M.D. (1986 - 1988) (interim position)
5. Russell Chesney, M.D. (1988 -   )

Deceased (as of December 31, 2002)

Appendix F
Chiefs of Staff
Le Bonheur Children's Medical Center, Inc.
(and the years they served)

*Dr. F. Tom Mitchell (1952 - 1955)

*Dr. C. Barton Etter (1956 - 1958)

*Dr. James G. Hughes (1959 - 1960)

*Dr. James N. Ettledorf (1961 - 1964)

Dr. Steve Turnbull (1965 - 1966)

Dr. George Lovejoy (1967 - 1968)

Dr. Raphael N. Paul (1969 - 1970)

Dr. Joseph Rothschild (1971 - 1972)

Dr. Robert B. Miller (1973 - 1974)

Dr. Earle L. Wrenn, Jr. (1975 - 1976)

Dr. Gene L. Whitington (1977 - 1978)

*Dr. Robert G. Allen (1979 - 1980)

*Dr. Lloyd V. Crawford (1981 - 1982)

Dr. Robert S. Hollabaugh (1983 - 1984)

Dr. Emmett D. Bell, Jr. (1985 - 1986)

Dr. Charles W. Gross (1987 - 1988)

Dr. S. Douglas Hixson (1989 - 1990)

Dr. Robert W. Riiklola (1991 - 1992)

Dr. Robert S. Hollabaugh (1993 - 1994)

Dr. Noel K. Frizzell (1995 - 1996)

Dr. H. Norman Noe (1997 - 1998)

Dr. Stephanie A. Storgion (1999 - 2000)

Dr. Gerald R. Jerkins (2001 - 2002)

*Deceased (as of December 31, 2002)

Appendix G
Chief Residents
Le Bonheur Children's Medical Center, Inc.

(and the years they served)

Emmett Bell (1954)

Fred Pipkin (1955)

Robert Meadows (1956)

Gene Whitington (1957)

Fred Grogan, Jr. (1958)

Walter Hughes (1959)

Cecil Jenkins (1960)

Bobby Higgs (1961)

Hershel Wall (1962)

Carroll Howard (1963)

John McEachin (1964)

Charles Raper (1965)

Larry Patton (1966)

Luis Navarro, Jr. (1967)

Jerry Campbell (1968)

Herman Crisler (1969)

Robert Dillard (1970)

Richard Butler (1971)

Robert Walling (1972)

Graham Rose (1973)

Peter Whitington (1974)

D. Jeannette Martin (1975)

Larry Faust (1976)

Thad Woodard (1977)

John Williams (1978)

James Brasfield (1979)

Michael Blaiss (1980)

Evelyn Suttle (1981)

Donna Swain (1982)

Glenn Silber (1983)

Stephen Smith (1984)

Cathy Stevens (1985)

Tara Burnette (1986)

Timothy Gillespie (1987)

Betty Mirro (1988)

Aimee` Christian (1989)

Rita Westbrook (1990)

Stephen Spooner (1991)

Jane Sneed (1992)

Deborah Nelson (1993)

Steven Barron (1994)

John DiMichelle (1995)

Charles Hanson (1996)

Virginia Coreil (1997)

Pemmaraju Dakin (1998)

Michael Lacy (1999)

John Doty (2000)

Barbara Summers (2001)

Cassandra Howard (2002)

Eddie Thomas (2002)

Appendix H
Employees of the Year
Le Bonheur Children's Medical Center, Inc.

1969	Alice Patton
1970	Eugene Tarver
1971	Gladys Brown
1972	Doris Bayles
1973	Leola Woods
1974	Mary Williams
1975	David Dunlap
1976	Mary Caldwell
1977	Margie Whitney
1978	Johnnie Hoggard
1979	Wilford Price
1980	Virginia Sloan
1981	Imogene Leavy
1982	Leo Cranford
1983	George East
1984	Mary Snipes
1985	Vernia Mae Lemons
1986	Shirley Smith
1987	Erma Paydon
1988	Arthur Johnson
1989	Catherine Hobson
1990	Jim Morgan
1991	Lue Brown
1992	Joe Green
1993	Eulila Flinn
1994	Lee Brown
1995	Patricia Jones
1996	Robert Edwards, Jr.